PRAISE FOR

The Art and Science of EMDR

"As an EMDR trainer, I always felt there was a need for a book that explained EMDR and its underlying neurology in easy-to-understand language. Rotem Brayer has created the perfect book that lives somewhere between Shapiro's foundational text and the EMDR training manual. I will be recommending *The Art and Science of EMDR* to every therapist I train."

> **—Andrew Dobo, PhD,** EMDRIA approved trainer and author of *The Hero's Journey: Integrating Jungian Psychology and EMDR Therapy* and *Unburdening Souls at the Speed of Thought*

"Rotem Brayer has artfully managed to welcome EMDR clinicians into the dialogue about the science of EMDR, while simultaneously empowering them to trust their own humanity as healers. This is a much-needed addition to the canon of EMDR literature!"

> **—Marshall Lyles, LMFT-S, LPC-S, RPT-S,** EMDR consultant and coauthor of *Advanced Sandtray Therapy: Digging Deeper into Clinical Practice*

"*The Art and Science of EMDR* is a robust, practical resource for any EMDR therapist searching for a deeper understanding of this powerful type of therapy in an easy-to-digest format. Rotem Brayer has created a clinical staple for us with this one!"

> **—Jackie Flynn, EdS, LMHC-S, RPT,** EMDR certified, EMDRIA approved consultant

"*The Art and Science of EMDR* is a breath of fresh air, a call to the future from the new generation of EMDR practitioners, trainers, and consultants, willing and able to develop and grow this therapy in every direction it now needs to go. Full of practical ideas and invitations, from therapist self-care and mindfulness/meditation to neuroscience and interweaves for challenging clients, Rotem Brayer's approach invites especially the more newly trained therapist to make EMDR their own, grounded in Shapiro's core structure but embracing the relationship and the dance— the art indeed, as well as the science. This book is well worth adding to the frontline therapist's toolkit."

>   **—Mark Brayne,** EMDR consultant and author of *Unleash Your EMDR:*
>   *Release the Magic: A Guidebook for Attachment-Informed, Integrative,*
>   *Transpersonal EMDR*

"The much-anticipated book *The Art and Science of EMDR* is a natural extension of what many clinicians who have followed his podcast have come to appreciate about Rotem Brayer: a curious and heartfelt integration of both the scientific and interpersonal elements of good therapy. Rotem is not bewildered by the complexity of the neuroscience that underpins all we love about EMDR therapy, and he takes a conversational and highly readable tone throughout. In particular, the chapters on mindfulness and an attuned processing approach hold the promise of demystifying and deprotocolizing solid EMDR practice for the reader. An excellent tool for EMDR consultants as well!"

>   **—Ann Beckley-Forest, LCSW-R, RPT-S,** EMDR approved consultant and
>   trainer, and coeditor of *EMDR with Children in the Play Therapy Room: An*
>   *Integrated Approach*

"This book feels like having an EMDR coach in your pocket. Rotem Brayer takes you through each phase and tells you the truth about what can happen during EMDR. As I read through *The Art and Science of EMDR* I kept thinking, *I never knew this, this is so interesting,* and *this graphic helps explain this concept.* This book is a beautiful roadmap to working with EMDR. I'm so grateful to Brayer for generously creating this and giving so much helpful information!"

—Jocelyn Fitzgerald, LMFT, ATR-BC, EMDR consultant and coauthor and coeditor of *EMDR Creative Arts Therapies*

"*The Art and Science of EMDR* is a must-have for EMDR-trained therapists who are looking to gain confidence in their facilitation of EMDR with clients. This easy-to-read book can help therapists educate clients about EMDR, as well as deepen their own understanding of the EMDR process. *The Art and Science of EMDR* is going to be my first recommendation for newly trained EMDR therapists looking to enhance their understanding, practice, and confidence in providing EMDR therapy."

—Stephanie Heitkemper, PhD, LPC, RPT, FT, EMDR certified and EMDRIA approved consultant

The Art and Science of
EMDR

HELPING CLINICIANS

BRIDGE THE PATH FROM

PROTOCOL TO PRACTICE

ROTEM BRAYER, MEd, LPC

Published by
PESI Publishing, Inc.
3839 White Ave
Eau Claire, WI 54703

Cover and Interior Design: Emily Dyer
Editing: Jenessa Jackson, PhD

ISBN: 9781683736318 (print)
ISBN: 9781683736325 (ePUB)
ISBN: 9781683736332 (ePDF)

About the Author

Rotem Brayer, MEd, LPC, is a certified EMDR therapist, EMDR consultant, and advanced EMDR trainer. He is the founder of The EMDR Learning Community (emdr-learning.com), a community that brings EMDR therapists together and provides education on EMDR therapy and the integration of this modality with other treatment approaches. As the cofounder of EMDR Denver, a practice that helps clients heal with an "EMDR first" approach, Rotem divides his time between consulting on cases, coaching EMDR therapists, and helping clients heal from the effects of trauma and attachment wounds.

Table of Contents

Acknowledgments

In this book, I share my passion for EMDR excellence. My desire to share this knowledge with therapists around the world could not have come to fruition without the help, guidance, and support of many great people.

I would like to first thank all my past and present clients. You are my best teachers, and I feel honored that you've allowed me into your inner worlds.

To my wife, Laura, and my children, Noam and Ari, you keep inspiring me with your joy, passion, and love for life. Having you in my world has given life deeper meaning.

To my mentors, Dr. Andrew Dobo, Jay Fellers, and Dr. Jamie Marich, I am so grateful to you for sharing your wisdom and compassion with me. I especially appreciate the inspiration to be authentic and to think outside the box, and to always look for creative ways to help my clients and consultees.

I am also grateful for many colleagues and friends who share my passions for EMDR excellence and for developing a community for EMDR therapists around the world. Jackie Flynn—my ventral vagal friend—I am constantly inspired by your knowledge, wisdom, and passion for sharing. I feel blessed to have you as my friend and appreciate your support for building a community and guiding others along their path to EMDR mastery.

To my therapist, Kate, who taught me that good therapy, EMDR or not, always starts with an authentic therapist and a meaningful relationship. I am grateful to have you as my therapist.

To all the guests and contributors to The Art and Science of EMDR community, Katie Smith, Laura Casey-Foss, Mark Brayne, Dr. Debbie Korn, Michael Baldwin, Mara Tesler-Stein, Adam O'Brien, Patrick Weeg, Dr. Arielle Schwartz, Craig Penner, Dr. John Hartung, Rebecca Strong, Amie Luyties, Dr. Robert Tinker, Jeremy Fox, Dr. Linda Homeyer, Marshall Lyles, Mariah Rooney, Sadie Smith, Kelly Smyth-Dent, Annie Monaco, Ann Beckley-Forest,

Dr. Stephen Dansiger, Dr. Howard Lipke, Rachel Walker, Karby Allington-Goldfain, Sue Seiler, Robin Shapiro, Reg Morrow-Robinson, Bill Brislin, Jillian Hosey, Sherri Jacobs, Peggy Kolodny, and Elizabeth Davis, thank you for your contributions and your willingness to generously share your knowledge and passion for healing with our community.

To Dr. Polona Curk, thank you for all the guidance and support at the beginning stages of my writing.

To my book coach, Marisa Solis, I can't thank you enough for helping me turn the thousands of ideas in my brain into a coherent narrative, outline, and eventually, book proposal. Your wisdom, knowledge, and caring have been apparent throughout the whole process of writing this book.

To my team at PESI Publishing, Kate Sample, Karsyn Morse, and Jenessa Jackson, thank you so much for all your feedback, support, and guidance. I could not have asked for a better team to work with to bring this book to life. Thank you for allowing me to keep my original tone and bringing your expertise in editing, publishing, and marketing.

....

Foreword

....

I wrote the book *EMDR Made Simple: Four Approaches to Using EMDR with Every Client* for PESI Publishing in 2011, several years before Rotem Brayer even trained as an EMDR therapist. When I had the privilege of meeting Rotem many years later, through his work on *The Art and Science of EMDR* podcast, it delighted me to learn that he considers *EMDR Made Simple* influential on his development as an EMDR therapist. So it feels like a very full circle experience to be writing a foreword for Rotem's first book, also being released into the world by PESI Publishing!

In getting to know Rotem over the last several years, I have found a true friend in the EMDR community. Rotem is committed to technical excellence, yet he also approaches EMDR, and all trauma therapy, with a practicality and friendliness that is sometimes missing in the EMDR therapy community. His commitment to both the art and science of EMDR is something that I admire. And I know that readers of his book are going to benefit from his skill at blending these perspectives as he helps them to cut through a lot of confusing messages that they might receive coming out of basic training or developing as advanced EMDR therapists. For EMDR therapy veterans, my hope is that you will be inspired by Rotem's enthusiasm and recognize that often it's the relative newcomers to the EMDR table that have the most to teach us. Many people described me in that way when I wrote *EMDR Made Simple*, and I'm now very proud to be the EMDR veteran who describes my friend in this way.

The Art and Science of EMDR is being released at a very important time in EMDR therapy's evolution. Even though we've shifted from thinking of EMDR largely as a technique to more of a comprehensive treatment approach, there are voices in the EMDR community who continue to push the science as supreme and to refine the various technical offshoots stemming from EMDR therapy. While I certainly don't disparage innovation, many of these voices and movements are downplaying the importance of the therapeutic relationship in EMDR therapy, which concerns me a great deal. Rotem is someone who is interested in the innovations yet remembers that therapy, at its core, is a relational endeavor.

Yes, I've authored three books on EMDR therapy and am well known in my work as a foundational and advanced topics trainer in EMDR therapy. Yet at the end of the day, I am a person who is out and proud about my own struggles with mental health and addiction disorders, and I evaluate thought leaders by how they make me feel as a person. Rotem is someone with whom I feel very safe and respected, and these are qualities that I need in a teacher. I hope that you will discover these qualities in Rotem and his approach as you work through the pages of *The Art and Science of EMDR*.

—**Jamie Marich,** PhD, LPCC-S, REAT, RYT-500, RMT

Introduction

To redeem one person is to redeem the whole world.
—The Talmud

Let me start by asking you a couple questions: What makes some EMDR therapists better than others? Why is it that some EMDR therapists get a lot of "positive outcomes" when working with their clients, while others always feel stuck? The answers to both questions are the same: practice and experience. The good news is, if you are a practitioner who struggles to achieve the EMDR outcomes you desire, there is a method for getting better—and this book will show you how to do it.

This guide is designed with one goal in mind: to help you become a more confident and more competent EMDR therapist. The truth is that many therapists train in EMDR but become confused and overwhelmed when they put it into practice. Some find it "too regimented" and become discouraged by having to always follow a rigid protocol. Others are afraid to mess up, say the wrong thing, or make their clients feel worse. Many also fear working with dissociative clients or are unsure how to find the right target or the right interweave. These struggles often characterize new therapists who are fresh out of basic EMDR training, though it also applies to seasoned therapists who, despite good intentions to learn and grow, sometimes continue to struggle.

So what is needed to become a competent and confident EMDR therapist? First, you must learn to see the phase-based model more holistically. Second, you must learn some basic concepts and complementary strategies. Third, you must practice, practice, practice. No matter how many books you read or how many trainings you take, your growth as an EMDR therapist will improve only when you start to practice.

The Art and Science of EMDR is designed to help you improve your EMDR practice, no matter where you are on your EMDR journey. Both newbie and experienced EMDR therapists can benefit from understanding the concepts described in this book and implementing the suggested practice methods to improve treatment outcomes. EMDR consultants can benefit from learning about the most common issues that therapists run into and, more importantly, from implementing deliberate practice in their own consultations.

This book is not a substitute for EMDR training, nor does it attempt to be a comprehensive review of EMDR therapy. I assume you've already read the latest edition of Francine Shapiro's *Eye Movement Desensitization and Reprocessing (EMDR) Therapy* and that you have the fundamentals of the EMDR process down. However, reading this book can guide you to get the most out of *any* stage of your EMDR journey—basic training, consultation, or even advanced training. Here is what you will learn in *The Art and Science of EMDR*:

- **Chapter 1: Your Brain on EMDR**—You'll learn what makes changes in the brain possible and how you can use the power of neuroplasticity to improve clinical outcomes when working with EMDR clients.

- **Chapter 2: How EMDR Works**—You'll get a better understanding of the mechanics of EMDR, including what happens in the brain and body when you're resourcing your clients and doing active processing.

- **Chapter 3: The Therapeutic Relationship in EMDR**—Because basic EMDR training does not adequately address this topic, this chapter will help you discover why it's crucial to build and maintain strong therapeutic rapport. You'll also review specific actions you can take to improve the therapist-client relationship.

- **Chapter 4: Preparation Done Better**—You'll be surprised by the most common mistakes EMDR therapists make during the preparation phase, and you'll learn what you can do to improve your preparation and resourcing work.

- **Chapter 5: EMDR and Mindfulness**—EMDR is an integrative approach that includes an important mindfulness component. You will learn why "a brain on mindfulness" is more likely to benefit from EMDR work. You'll also gain tools to help your clients become more mindful. Most importantly, you will learn why a mindful therapist is a better therapist.

- **Chapter 6: Setting the Ground for Effective Processing**—In order to do effective EMDR work, you don't have to give up your authenticity. You will learn how to maintain your authentic self, conceptualize EMDR as a holistic approach, improve your assessment, and prepare yourself to do processing work with your clients.

- **Chapter 7: Where the Magic of EMDR Happens**—You will discover the most common mistakes made by EMDR therapists when actively processing target memories. And you'll learn how to enhance your processing and help clients overcome obstacles, like looping and dissociating. Some techniques, different from those you've learned in basic EMDR training, will help you take your EMDR processing to the next level.

- **Chapter 8: Deliberate Practice**—The necessity of methodical practice is by far the most important thing you can take from this book. By following the rules of deliberate practice—an approach that experts in a wide range of fields use to improve performance—you will learn how to bring the science of learning and performance into your EMDR practice.

My confidence in your ability to continue growing as an EMDR therapist stems not only from my research and my own work as a therapist but also from my experience doing individual and group consultations. As an EMDR consultant, I often watch individuals who lack confidence turn into highly capable and strong EMDR therapists after implementing the methods I describe here. The lessons in this book, along with deliberate practice, will be a game changer in your growth as an EMDR clinician too.

EMDR gives you the power to help clients heal from traumatic and distressing memories and experiences. It's your duty, as an EMDR therapist, to always push forward and take your EMDR practice to the next level. This book will show you how.

CHAPTER 1

Your Brain on EMDR

. . . .

*When negative reactions and behaviors in the present can be
tracked directly back to an earlier memory, we define those
memories as "unprocessed"—meaning that they are stored
in the brain in a way that still holds the emotions, physical
sensations, and beliefs that were experienced earlier in life.*

—Francine Shapiro, *Getting Past Your Past*

. . . .

Your Plastic Brain

If you've ever been involved in the never-ending debate of "which therapy works better," or if you've ever wondered what makes a certain type of therapy more effective, you don't have to guess anymore. Thanks to neuroscience and the ability to look inside the brain, we now know exactly what makes the difference between the forms of therapy that lead to long-term, sustainable results and those that are just not as effective: **Therapy is effective when it produces neurological changes in the brain. When brain cells change their activation patterns, neural networks start the process of integration. Therefore, therapy produces the most sustainable results when it changes the brain.**

Until fairly recently, mainstream scientists believed that the adult brain does not change and that the anatomy of the brain was fixed after childhood. But in the early 1990s, Alvaro Pascual-Leone, a medical doctor with a PhD in physiology, conducted a series of experiments that demonstrated how neural networks change as a result of repetition of certain activities. Pascual-Leone used transcranial magnetic stimulation (TMS) to map the brains of blind individuals who learned how to read Braille. He found that as learners developed better skills, measured by their ability to read more words per minute, specific neural networks increased in size. I will discuss this study in more detail in chapter 4, but for now, remember that repetition of an activity (physical or mental) leads to a strengthening of specific neural networks.

Since this time, a growing body of research has clearly shown that the brain is "plastic," meaning that under certain conditions, the brain can change its own structure. These studies show that certain activities (therapy included) can lead to massive rewiring of the brain (Cowan & Kandel, 2001; Cozolino, 2015, 2017; Doidge, 2007). In addition, thanks to advances in brain imaging technology and the development of tools like functional magnetic resonance imaging (fMRI) and positron emission tomography (PET), scientists can now see what happens inside the brain in real time as well as over a period of time. The conclusions drawn from all this data are definite: The most effective therapies lead to a trait change, which is a long-lasting alteration of neurons and neural networks—and, as a result, a more integrated brain (more on this in chapter 4).

Therefore, before I get to the EMDR protocol, its eight phases, and the many challenges therapists face when using EMDR, it's important to understand how this treatment leads to the integration of neural networks. In the pages that follow, you will develop an understanding of how maladaptive neural networks form, including how trauma alters the brain and what you can do as a therapist to change that. Understanding the brain's ability to create new neural pathways—and taking advantage of the brain's plasticity—will help you make informed decisions in session when treating your EMDR clients.

Neural Networks

The human brain contains about 100 billion brain cells, called neurons. Each neuron is a biological switch. When they become activated, or "fire," neurons send and receive electric signals to and from neighboring neurons and, in doing so, form neural networks. When it comes to memory reprocessing, it's important to understand that specific memories are stored in specific neural networks.

In particular, the brain stores information in a complex collection of neural networks "where related memories are physically connected to one another so that activation of any memory in the network will tend to activate others in that network" (Zadra & Stickgold, 2021, p. 103).

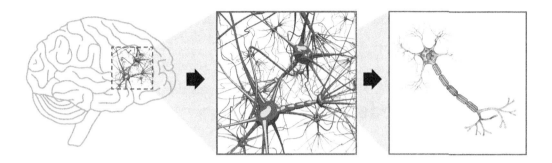

The neural networks involved in the formation and retrieval of specific memories were demonstrated by a team of American and Israeli researchers (Gelbard-Sagiv et al., 2008). In their study, participants were asked to watch a series of short videos while they had electrodes connected to their brains. After taking a break, the participants were asked to recall the videos they watched. The neural firing patterns of an individual subject varied from video to video, which should come as no surprise. But when subjects were asked to recall a specific video, their brains showed the same exact neural activity as when they originally watched the video.

What the results of this study mean to EMDR is that when you ask clients to describe a trauma memory—using images, thoughts, emotions, and body sensations—you activate the same network of neurons that fired when the disturbing memory originally happened. Because neurons that fire together wire together (Hebb, 1949), these maladaptive neural networks have strengthened their connections over time, leading to the symptoms that caused these clients to seek therapy. In EMDR, the goal is to intentionally activate these maladaptive neural networks and rewire them so they can become integrated with more adaptive networks. Effective EMDR therapy is done with the understanding of how neural firing patterns change so you can facilitate these changes in your clients' brains.

Before we talk further about how trauma can impact the brain, I want to mention one specific neural network, or "network of networks," that we all share. This network's default mode of operation is what causes so many clients to struggle with rumination and feelings of inadequacy. Scientists simply call it the *default mode network*, or DMN. Recent research reveals that some of the effects of EMDR can be explained by recruiting and activating parts of this network. Let's take a look.

The Default Mode Network

The DMN was discovered by accident, when Marcus Raichle (2001), a neurologist from Washington University, noticed something interesting that happened right before he started his experiments. In order to establish baseline for participants' brain activity, Raichle and his team instructed their subjects to "do nothing." During this time, Raichle noticed a pattern of increased activity in a brain region that he would later call the DMN.

As Raichle's work illustrated, the DMN becomes active when the mind is at passive rest, which makes it more likely to wander and daydream. When that happens, people can get caught up in ruminating about the past or worrying about the future (Pollan, 2018), as opposed to focusing on what is happening in the here and now. Ever wonder why children are so skilled at being in the present moment while most adults struggle with doing so? One explanation is that a child's DMN is not fully developed, so they don't spend as much time in mental time-travel and self-reflection.

As therapists, we often attribute rumination to anxiety, depression, or trauma because clients with these conditions often struggle to slow down their thoughts. But some people ruminate simply due to an overactive DMN—without meeting criteria for any psychiatric diagnosis. Without the need to pathologize or diagnose, EMDR can be used to target the subject of rumination and alleviate unnecessary suffering for any client, regardless of diagnosis. In other words, you don't need to find trauma to justify the effective use of EMDR. However, if trauma does exist, there is no better therapeutic approach to healing it other than EMDR. Let's take a quick look into how EMDR can help resolve trauma.

Your Brain on Trauma

As you grow your EMDR proficiency, you will learn advanced skills and techniques for treating developmental trauma and attachment wounds. While maintaining this level of proficiency is especially important if you are seeing clients with a history of complex trauma, the following section is designed to offer only a brief introduction to EMDR and trauma. For a more in-depth dive into how to treat this specific population of clients, please see the resources at the end of this book. (You can also visit https://emdartnscience.com/book for an online directory of these resources.)

Psychiatrist and trauma expert Bessel van der Kolk (2015) describes trauma not just as an event that happened in the past but also as any "imprint left by that experience on mind, brain, and body" (p. 21). This distinction is important. When you treat a client with a history of trauma, you are not changing their past, but you are changing the effects that the past left on their brain and nervous system—and, as a result, on their psyche.

These effects of the past are ever-present, as trauma survivors tend to respond to reminders of the trauma as if the trauma were still happening right now. For example, they may be triggered by certain sounds (e.g., footsteps, sirens), or they may become extremely agitated at the sight of an angry face, even if the anger is not directed toward them. The traumatized brain automatically reacts to reminders of the trauma—to these triggers—in a similar way to how it responded to the original threat. Trauma survivors, in large part, respond this way because their brains become wired to detect danger. The trauma becomes imprinted in their limbic systems, and especially their amygdalae,* which are the brain's threat detectors.

For those individuals who have experienced repeated trauma, the brain reacts even more severely—more wiring around danger leads to a rigid and overreactive limbic system in which a person's sensitivity to threat becomes further generalized. For example, it is common for soldiers who come back from war to be hypersensitive to loud sounds. As they have been repeatedly exposed to

---

* Although many people use the term *amygdala* when referring to this brain structure, there are actually two amygdalae in the brain: one in each hemisphere.

these kinds of sounds in combat, their brains learn to associate loud noises with life-threatening situations.

Trauma that happens in early childhood, especially if repeated, results in the most severe symptoms, as the brain is at the peak of its plasticity during this period. When a child experiences repeated patterns of danger, or even *perceived* danger, the brain learns to generalize and be fearful of every perceived threat, even when a threat is not real or not present. For example, a young girl who was repeatedly sexually assaulted by her uncle may conclude that all men are dangerous because her limbic system is on overdrive, especially when seeing, interacting with, or even thinking of men. Thus, clients who were abused and neglected during the first few years of life have the most severe trauma symptoms, as early childhood is a critical period for the development of neural networks associated with emotion regulation (specifically between the amygdalae and the prefrontal cortex). These networks develop optimally when nurturing, attuned caregivers meet a young child's emotional needs. But when these networks fail to develop as a result of trauma, the individual develops a limited ability to regulate their emotions, resulting in symptoms of anxiety, depression, or any other "disorder" that motivates clients to seek therapy. For many individuals, this unbearable suffering is linked to those early childhood attachment wounds.

The Limits of Language

Helping clients find words to describe their traumas is not an easy task. Words often fail to express how trauma survivors feel because trauma, by definition, is nonverbal. And even when clients can find the words to express the pain that the trauma has caused, talk therapies can only offer so much relief because they do not affect the neurological changes that happened as a result of the trauma. The language center of the brain (Broca's area) is located in the front of the brain, but trauma, on the other hand, is stored deep inside the brain, in the form of implicit memories. Therefore, resolution of trauma requires a deeper, more comprehensive approach.

Luckily, where talk-based, language-focused therapies fail, EMDR can help by targeting the areas of the brain where implicit memories are stored. It can literally rewire some of the nonverbal parts of the brain and help deactivate the amygdalae (de Voogd et al., 2018). This is why EMDR is also known as "limbic system therapy" (van der Kolk, 2015, p. 205). It helps clients when words themselves are not enough. In the next chapter, I will discuss in more detail how EMDR works, how it rewires the limbic system, and why it is one of the most effective ways to heal trauma.

CHAPTER 2

How EMDR Works

. . . .

*As the dialogue between psychotherapy and neuroscience
continues to evolve, an increasing number of new scientific
findings will be applied to theory and practice.*

—Louis Cozolino, *The Neuroscience of Psychotherapy*

. . . .

The Adaptive Information Processing (AIP) Model

I've already established that EMDR changes neural networks in the brain, but how does this magic happen? How does focusing on a target memory while engaging in bilateral eye movements or holding two vibrating pulsators lead to actual changes in the brain? In this chapter, I will answer these questions by taking a closer look at the mechanics of EMDR.

To start, it's important to understand that every time people retrieve a memory, they can potentially change or adjust that memory. Peter Levine (2015) calls memory a "reconstructive process" (p. 3), which means that when clients recall an event while feeling stressed, they add the current stressful energy to the memory. As a result, the next time—and any subsequent time—they retrieve the same memory, it is likely to have this additional stressful energy attached to it. I will expand on this idea in the next chapter in the context of the therapeutic relationship, but for now, remember that "memory is a reconstructive process that is continuously selecting, adding, deleting, rearranging, and updating information" (Levine, 2015, p. 3).

Generally, the brain can be divided into three main areas: the thinking brain, the feeling brain, and the sensing brain. In talk therapy, clients mostly stay in their thinking brain (their prefrontal cortex) while occasionally engaging their feeling brain (their limbic system) and rarely engaging the sensing brain (their brainstem). However, to optimize therapeutic outcomes, all three areas of the brain should be activated at the same time while using bilateral stimulation to activate natural healing processes that already exist in the brain. This is the basis of the adaptive information processing (AIP) model, which provides the theoretical framework behind EMDR.

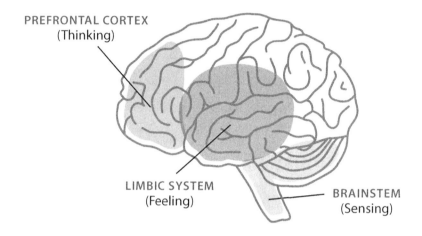

PREFRONTAL CORTEX
(Thinking)

LIMBIC SYSTEM
(Feeling)

BRAINSTEM
(Sensing)

To understand the AIP model, think about a mildly disturbing experience that happened to you over the past few months. Maybe a client ghosted you and you felt hurt, or maybe your spouse was dismissive when you needed to feel heard. Perhaps it felt really painful in the moment, but after a few days, you started feeling a little better. As time passed, the event continued to feel less disturbing because your brain processed the information and categorized it as something that happened in the past. As a result, a month later, it was just memory of something that happened and it stopped being in the forefront of your thoughts.

However, for clients who have experienced trauma, this natural healing mechanism is hindered because trauma and attachment wounds affect the brain's ability to process information. This can make the past feel like it is still the present. As a result, an event that happened a month ago, a year ago, or forty years ago can still hold the same (if not more) emotional charge. Your mission, as an EMDR therapist, is to support this natural healing mechanism—to facilitate the adaptive information processing—and allow healing to happen.

To stimulate the AIP system, ask your clients to notice any images, cognitions, emotions, or body sensations that arise as they retrieve a traumatic memory and engage in bilateral stimulation (BLS). The BLS is thought to allow for complete processing of the memory by activating a mechanism that naturally happens in the brain during rapid eye movement (REM) sleep—the intervals of sleep characterized by an increased heart rate, irregular breathing, dreaming, and as the name suggests, the fast movement of the eyes beneath the eyelids. Despite the body being asleep, the brain is highly active during REM sleep. Baldwin and Korn (2021) report that during REM sleep, the brain:

- Reduces negative emotions associated with memories

- Thinks more flexibly by building new associations between memories

- Is better at gaining insight from these new associations

Sound familiar? It's no coincidence that the EM of EMDR is the same EM of REM. Eye movements and other forms of BLS help facilitate the natural healing mechanisms of the brain.

One of the biggest challenges for beginner EMDR therapists is to trust this process (Parnell, 2006). As a therapist, it can be hard to let go of your own interpretations and resist the temptation to offer therapeutic interventions. It can also be difficult to let your clients "just notice" whatever arises as they tap into their trauma memories. Adopting the AIP model will help you to shift your mindset. It will allow you to trust the brain's capacity to heal.

The Reorganization of Memory Networks

In the previous chapter, I explored how neural networks strengthen their connections over time and that certain maladaptive networks can develop rigid neural firing patterns as a result. Many mental health symptoms develop this way, with most issues being the result of overactivity or underactivity in certain areas of the brain. For example, an overactive limbic system (specifically the amygdalae) can lead to anxiety, while an underactive prefrontal cortex is correlated with depression. Simply viewed, these symptoms come from rigid firing patterns of certain neural networks.

Sometimes these patterns can become inflexible mental representations of reality, as is often the case with trauma. Therefore, most clients can't heal trauma or other symptoms of mental health disorders by simply reframing their conscious thoughts or by using some surface-level interventions. They need your support to create new patterns in their brains.

In the next several sections, I will provide a better understanding of how EMDR therapy can change these neural firing patterns. Understanding your clients' issues through the lens of neuroscience not only helps destigmatize mental illnesses as a whole, but it can also help you work with more confidence as a therapist. As you will see throughout this book, knowing how memory networks are organized and how they can be *reorganized*—along with the healing that occurs as a result of this neural reorganization—will help you make better choices when treating clients.

The EMDR Therapist as a Neuroscientist

Since positive outcomes in psychotherapy are correlated with the growth and integration of neural networks, EMDR therapists must function as "applied neuroscientists" (Cozolino, 2017, p. 397) who familiarize themselves with the neuroscience of psychotherapy. You'll recall that trauma is stored in the brain in the form of implicit memories, over which clients have limited conscious awareness. Therefore, if you want to help your clients rewire the networks that activate their traumatic memories and heal their trauma-related symptoms, you first need to understand the difference between *implicit* and *explicit* memories.

Explicit memories involve those that you can intentionally and consciously recall. These memories are based on facts and have a coherent narrative. For example, our ability to remember what we had for dinner last night, or facts we memorized for a presentation, are examples of explicit memories. In contrast, implicit memories operate outside of conscious awareness and cannot be recalled as stories or facts. These types of memories are automatic and often appear as a series of physical sensations and emotions that show up without warning. For example, a client who was physically abused at a young age may experience unexplained anger and abdominal pain in adulthood when confronted by a colleague who has similar physical features as their abuser. Since the networks that store implicit memories operate below the level of consciousness and are not accessible to the conscious mind, EMDR is helpful in accessing, retrieving, and changing them.

EMDR does so by promoting integration between the left and the right hemispheres, which leads to changes in traumatic memories that become more explicit. The mechanisms of action explaining the effects of EMDR are complex, and new theories continue to emerge (Calancie et al., 2018). Fortunately, to be an effective EMDR therapist, you don't need to know the latest research on its mechanisms of action. Instead, you have to remember these basic principles:

If you want EMDR therapy to be effective, you have to activate the thinking brain, the emotional brain, and the sensing brain simultaneously while generating moderate states of arousal. I will talk in more detail about how to achieve this level of arousal in chapter 7, when I discuss the window of tolerance, but know that moderate levels of arousal lead to the production of neurotransmitters and neural growth, which optimize neuroplasticity (Cozolino, 2017).

For many therapists, it can feel uncomfortable to think about what we do in technical terms. Your work is not as linear as that of a neuroscientist, and you don't have measures to evaluate the outcomes of your work the same way scientists do. Many therapists tend to think of themselves more as artists than scientists, but you have to keep in mind that good therapy requires you to use both the rational and emotional parts of your brain.

The EMDR Therapist as a Healer

Most Western medical and mental health professionals don't use the word *healing* to describe what they do, but that is precisely what you are doing in the context of EMDR. The word *heal* originates from the Old English word *haelan*, which means "to make whole" (Doidge, 2015). Healing is a natural outcome of an integrated brain and can be simply viewed as the result of a more coherent system. When healing occurs, it leads to increased coherence among different structures in the brain, better interaction between the left and right hemispheres, and better communication between the brain and the heart (Childre & Rozman, 2005).

As an EMDR therapist, you can look at the outcome of your work and consider it as healing because successful EMDR therapy results in a system that operates more holistically. The end goal of EMDR is *adaptive resolution*—an elimination of symptoms, a resolution of the underlying trauma, and a coherent brain. When EMDR treatment successfully ends with adaptive resolution, clients experience an elimination of symptoms and a shift in memories such that they become more neutral and less emotional. If I haven't convinced you that what EMDR therapists do is healing, consider the words of David Servan-Schreiber (2005) as he describes healing: "To me, 'healing' means that patients are no longer suffering from the symptoms that they complained of when they first consulted, and that these symptoms do not come back after the treatment has been completed" (p. 11).

Remember that the words *treatment* and *healing* are not synonymous. Effective treatment, like EMDR, activates the natural healing mechanisms that already exist in the body but were simply "stuck." In other words, treatment will facilitate healing, but the capacity for healing is already present.

To be a healer, you don't have to be a witch doctor or a shaman. Your EMDR work promotes healing, whether you call it "adaptive resolution" (Shapiro, 2001, 2018), "homeostatic balance" (Cozolino, 2017), or "healing." In the next chapter, I will explore how to begin the process of healing in the therapy space and focus on the therapeutic relationship as a primary vehicle for healing.

Explaining EMDR to Your Clients

One of the most common struggles for both beginner and experienced EMDR clinicians is explaining to clients how EMDR works. By now, you hopefully have greater clarity on how EMDR helps rewire maladaptive neural networks, including its potential to heal trauma and eliminate symptoms through adaptive resolution, but how do you explain all that to your clients?

Unfortunately, too many therapists try to explain how EMDR works by using phrases like "long-term potentiation" or by talking about the effects of

BLS on brain areas such as the left medial frontal gyrus or the right precuneus. If your clients are not neuroscientists (and most clients aren't), they are likely to get confused by these terms or be unable to project these ideas onto their own issues. Instead, break down the concepts you just learned in a simpler manner. In particular, explain how EMDR helps increase integrative capacities by improving communication between the right and left hemispheres. In the most simple way, EMDR helps the different areas of the brain communicate better, which allows clients to turn disturbing memories into objective memories.

The key to providing a clear explanation of how EMDR works is to practice doing just that. Take a video of yourself as if you were explaining EMDR therapy to a client and watch it. Make sure your explanation sounds clear, and if there are points you need to improve, take some notes and record it again. Keep doing this until you feel confident in your ability to deliver "an elevator pitch" on the mechanisms behind EMDR. This will help your clients trust you and the process. And trust is the first step in building a strong therapeutic relationship.

CHAPTER 3

The Therapeutic Relationship in EMDR

. . . .

At its very core, the flow of therapy should be spontaneous, forever following unanticipated riverbeds; it is grotesquely distorted by being packaged into a formula that enables inexperienced, inadequately trained therapists (or computers) to deliver a uniform course of therapy.

—Irvin D. Yalom, *The Gift of Therapy*

. . . .

What Makes Therapy Work

Seasoned therapists with clinical experience will tell you that the therapeutic relationship is the most important factor in facilitating change in clients—and years of psychological research can back up this claim. In fact, hundreds of studies have shown that the quality of this relationship is the main predictor of successful treatment (Norcross, 2011; Orlinsky et al., 2004), with some studies suggesting that it predicts 97 percent of treatment outcomes (Baldwin et al., 2007).

So why do EMDR trainings, both basic and advanced, tend to dedicate minimal attention to discussing the importance of the therapeutic relationship or alliance? Establishing and strengthening this relationship between therapist and client takes time and effort, and EMDR therapy is no different.

In this chapter, I will explore the importance of the therapeutic relationship in the context of EMDR, with a specific focus on building and *maintaining* a strong relationship as a foundation for a successful EMDR treatment. I will also discuss why you often need more time to establish and *strengthen* this relationship with some clients (regardless of the phase you're in) and how to do that.

Developmental Trauma, Attachment Wounds, and the Therapeutic Relationship

From the day we are born, our brains seek connection with others. With very limited access to the external world, infants' brains are biologically hardwired to crave connection from their caregivers, who provide a foundation of safety, security, and comfort. However, when infants and young children suffer from an absence of connection and a repeated lack of attunement to their emotional and physical needs, they experience attachment ruptures that can lead to formation of deeper attachment wounds that follow them throughout life.

In fact, caregiver misattunement during a child's early years is one of the main contributors to the development of mental disorders. It's for this reason that many clients who seek help for mental distress suffer not only from "simple" trauma but from more complex developmental trauma and attachment wounds. Unfortunately, standard EMDR therapy is limited in its ability to help if the therapist-client relationship is not characterized by warmth, empathy, and unconditional positive regard. To provide better EMDR treatment and deliver better outcomes, you must keep the therapeutic alliance in the forefront of your mind, especially with clients who suffer from complex trauma and who were not fortunate enough to have caring, attuned caregivers in the first years of their lives.

When it comes to developing a strong therapeutic relationship with clients who have experienced complex, developmental trauma, these are the main characteristics that you need to focus on to facilitate attachment repair (Parnell, 2013):

- Ability to listen

- Ability to be present

- Ability to be attuned and empathetic

- Ability to sense body sensations

- Ability to attune and respond to nonverbal communication

- Ability to love and feel compassion while maintaining appropriate boundaries

- Ability to be playful, accepting, and curious

- Ability to be courageous and comfortable with strong emotions

- Ability to manage your own countertransference responses

- Knowledge of healthy child development

While some of these suggestions, such as listening, being attuned, and being empathetic, may seem obvious to you as a therapist, it can be difficult for many beginner EMDR therapists to keep these suggestions in mind when following a procedural script verbatim. As a result, many EMDR therapists miss the most important ingredient of quality therapy: the therapeutic relationship. However, being attuned to your clients' nonverbal experiences can make the difference between ineffective therapy and healing. Your clients need your help to repair their attachment wounds, so let's talk about how this repair happens.

How Repair Happens

Similar to trauma memories, early childhood memories are stored deep inside the brain and body in the form of implicit memories. That's because in the earliest years of life, children have not yet developed the capacity for language, so all their memories get encoded in preverbal form. If a child experiences disconnection and misattunement during these early years, they develop implicit memories that set their default mode to mistrust. As adults, they still hold these memories in the brain and body; these memories can manifest into a felt sense of isolation and an unspoken sense of being unlovable. It's for this reason that so many individuals with attachment wounds struggle to develop healthy relationships. Many have an internal felt sense of "there is something wrong with me" that they cannot understand or explain. More often than not, these limiting thoughts originate from early childhood experiences that clients don't remember.

These old memories are not explicitly accessible later in life because they have become isolated in their own memory networks that don't integrate with more adaptive networks of information. Therefore, you can't help clients address these memories by simply talking about them; they are not accessible through verbal language. Instead, the way to start changing the neural patterns that hold these attachment wounds is to help your clients feel safe and connected in the therapy room. When you give clients unconditional empathy and warmth, you help them develop a felt sense of safety in relationships which then becomes wired into their implicit, nonverbal neural networks. With this repeated sense of security, clients can start to slowly move away from their habitual mistrust—the beginning of the repair process.

To continue facilitating the repair process, Schore (2012) argues that therapists need to assume the role of *psychobiological regulators*, the same way that parents or caregivers help (or are supposed to help) regulate young children's emotions. By turning your full attention to your clients' emotional states, you do a lot more than instructing them to follow procedural steps or put their disturbance in a container. When you mirror their emotional expressions, tone of voice, posture, and physical sensations, you facilitate the process of repair. With your most vulnerable clients—those who need you to be their psychobiological regulator—any protocol, procedure, technique, or strategy is irrelevant until they can trust you and feel that you care.

However, changing nonverbal networks with care, empathy, and attunement is not an easy task. There are a couple of reasons for this. First, qualities such as attunement and warmth are things that clients can *feel* but cannot always explain. The correlation between how much you care about a client and the degree to which they get better is not always apparent. Measuring attunement is not easy. Second, this work can be hard because it requires you to sync with your clients' inner worlds. As a therapist, you often feel what your clients feel, including pain, heartache, grief, and anger. When you are constantly in this position of witnessing and holding difficult content, it can result in your own compassion fatigue or vicarious trauma that makes it difficult to be present with your clients.

This was an experience I learned shortly after working with Haddas, who was one of my first EMDR clients. A female refugee from Kenya, Haddas experienced horrendous traumas as an adult that were considerably more intense than anything I had heard before. But with a decade of experience in treating clients with complex trauma, I felt confident in my ability to handle Haddas's story. I considered myself immune to the effects of her traumatic experiences on me.

However, a few weeks after I started seeing Haddas, I started experiencing the effects of vicarious trauma. I started having nightmares. She had shared with me that her children were brutally tortured in front of her while she was forced to watch. As my own son was just a few months old at this time, it triggered something in me. My brain sent me clear signals that Haddas's traumas were starting to get wired into my own brain.

I needed help.

"Don't let her talk between sets. Just have her process the memories." This was the advice given to me by an experienced EMDR consultant. I was directed to focus on processing and minimize the talking. Desperate for help, I did my best to comply with my consultant's advice.

Back in session, I explained to Haddas that talking about her memories was not enough and that reprocessing these memories with EMDR therapy was the key to healing her traumas. I provided more information on how EMDR works and asked her to "just give me the headline" between BLS sets. It felt weird, but it worked! Haddas successfully processed her traumas, her reported levels of disturbance decreased, and her flashbacks and our nightmares stopped. I was convinced that this was the right way to do EMDR. I would ask my clients to talk less and process more.

But I very quickly realized that applying this strategy didn't always work. I learned that for many clients, asking them to *not* talk about what had happened felt retraumatizing. Many traumatized individuals don't have anyone they can talk to about their traumatic experiences. They need to be able to verbalize these experiences and their impacts. Having the ability to share their stories with a caring, empathetic therapist is a crucial element of healing.

If you find that a client's story is eliciting triggering reactions in you, make sure you take care of yourself. Vicarious trauma can resemble symptoms of primary trauma, and in some cases, secondary exposure can even cause a more serious reaction. Seek therapy and consultation, process your own experiences with a colleague, or connect with a community of therapists who support each other. And if your clients' traumas get wired into your own brain, you can do your own EMDR work to clear their trauma from your brain.

Clients with histories of complex developmental trauma need to know that EMDR is a treatment they will do together *with* you (Rosoff, 2019). They need to know that you welcome them to share their vulnerable experiences with you. To do so, you must create a safe and supportive environment by letting them talk as much or as little as they need. Most clients can heal only when they feel safety and connection. They need to know on every level that you care about them.

Regulate the Pace of Therapy

In addition to letting your clients talk, it is important to pay attention to the pace of therapy over the course of treatment as a whole. No two clients are the same, so no two therapy sessions should be the same either. Some EMDR leaders give the inflexible recommendation to process trauma within a small number of sessions, but this is unrealistic and can be dangerous, especially when working with more complex cases. Therapy cannot be one size fits all. Instead, you must personalize treatment by deeply attuning to and monitoring each client's ever-changing emotional states. This is crucial for EMDR treatment to be successful.

In basic EMDR training, you learned that during the preparation phase, you should focus primarily on teaching your clients tools and techniques for emotion regulation, such as the container exercise and the safe place. However, remember that the therapeutic relationship needs to come first, especially when working with clients who have complex trauma. It might take weeks, months, or even years to establish this relationship, but if clients do not feel safe with you, all your efforts in the preparation phase are doomed to fail.

Establishing a secure relationship with your clients, especially those who experienced attachment wounds or childhood trauma, is not a task that is limited to the preparation phase. The therapeutic relationship, like most relationships, is ever evolving. Some clients may need constant reassurance that they are safe with you. And when they don't feel safe, they will likely not share this verbally—you have to be able to notice and bring them back to the safety zone. Helping clients feel safe throughout all phases of EMDR is done by becoming a resource for your clients—by using co-regulation.

Become a Resource for Your Client: The Importance of Co-regulation

Many clients never learned how to be in a secure relationship, and the idea of feeling safe in any relationship feels foreign to them. In these cases, you need to be deliberate about using co-regulation to help them feel safe and connected. Co-regulation involves a collaboration between you and each of your clients, wherein you share your autonomic nervous system—all its resources, caring, and empathy—to help them feel safe, regulated, and grounded. When you co-regulate, you allow your clients to use you as their resource and return them to a state of safety.

When co-regulating, you become the psychobiological regulator that your clients need (Schore, 2015). For this to occur, clients must feel constant reassurance that you are present and attuned to their ever-changing emotions. This happens not only when they hear the words you speak but also—and this is important—when they hear your tone of voice and feel your presence and compassion. Your clients need to *sense* your conscious effort to let them in.

Additionally, your clients need to believe that their old wounds can be healed and to *feel* that you are hopeful about their ability to heal. A major part of your clients' ability to feel heard and understood, and their ability to feel your hope, occurs on a nonverbal level. In order to strengthen the therapeutic relationship, remember to pay attention to what happens nonverbally, on a body level, which surpasses the limitation of words. Finally, remember that what is regulating for one client can be dysregulating for another, so don't force connection if a certain client doesn't need it. Instead, focus on safety and choice.

The Relationship Is for the Client

Everything I've reviewed in this chapter is important for some clients, but not for all. While some clients will benefit tremendously from verbal expressions of empathy and a compassionate tone of voice, others may interpret it as dramatic and will sometimes feel uncomfortable as a result of your attempts to build rapport. Take, for example, Adam Cayton-Holland (2018), a comedian and the author of *Tragedy Plus Time*. He started EMDR therapy to process the memory of finding his sister's body following her suicide. In his book, he shares his experience as a client and describes his initial experience with his EMDR therapist:

> Eye Movement Desensitization and Reprocessing is an aggressive form of treatment used to help trauma victims, such as soldiers, affected by PTSD. But it can help anyone who's been through some shit. I gave it a try. As I sat with my new therapist on my initial intake she listened patiently and thoughtfully to my sob story, but kept her distance. With all the other shrinks I felt this immense sense of pity. It was cloying. They flinched and sighed dramatically with every detail of my story; they emoted and tried to show me how sympathetic they were. And I resented it. I was tired of people feeling sorry for me. I didn't need compassion. I needed help. This new doctor seemed relatively nonplussed. She wasn't unsympathetic, she said the appropriate things, but her attitude was one of yeah, fucked-up things happen, let's get to treating them. (pp. 174–175)

Therefore, while most clients will need you to become their psychobiological regulator—deliberately mirroring their emotions and nonverbal cues—for some clients, this may result in the opposite effect and cause them to leave therapy prematurely. Remember to get curious about your clients and what each needs as an individual. Then, based on the cues you get from them, customize your approach to the therapeutic relationship in an informed way.

CHAPTER 4

Preparation Done Better

. . . .

It is essential that we listen to and get to know each of our clients and adjust what we do according to each one's needs. In this way, we help to heal clients through attunement, connection and caring without re-injuring them through the imposition of a box or a label.

—Laurel Parnell, *Attachment-Focused EMDR*

. . . .

The #1 Mistake EMDR Therapists Make

Growing as an EMDR clinician requires making mistakes. All EMDR therapists, including trainers, consultants, and book authors, have had their fair share of EMDR mistakes. Therefore, it's not a matter of if you'll make mistakes—it's a matter of when and how you'll learn from them. If you don't learn from your mistakes, your EMDR practice will not improve, so give yourself permission to mess up, and know that most mistakes won't affect clients in a problematic way.

However, there is one critical mistake to avoid—one that has the potential to do harm—that many EMDR therapists make when they start using EMDR: They begin EMDR processing with clients who are not stable or well-resourced.

Unfortunately, some basic EMDR trainings do not emphasize the importance of the preparation phase enough, which can lead therapists to speed through this phase so they can begin processing more quickly. While both you and your clients may be eager to start processing, please remember (and tell your clients) that starting processing before they are ready can lead to adverse consequences, like destabilization, suicide attempts, psychiatric hospitalizations, or increased symptoms of anxiety and trauma.

In this chapter, you will learn how to apply resourcing throughout the entire therapy experience—a view that will help you develop a more holistic understanding of EMDR processing. You will also learn the importance of individualizing clients' inner resources and helping them create structure to practice their new coping skills so they can make the most out of them. I will review the importance of integrating somatic work with EMDR and explain how to identify contaminated resources. Finally, I will end the chapter by describing how to know when clients are ready for processing.

Resourcing Is Not Limited to the Preparation Phase

According to a linear EMDR model, once you are done with phase 1 (history taking), you move on to phase 2 (preparation), and then to phase 3 (assessment). By the time you get to phase 4, you are done with the first three phases, and clients are ready for desensitization. Right? Not so fast.

The linear model is one way to illustrate the basic concept of EMDR, but it can be helpful to change how you conceptualize EMDR. For instance, clients with complex trauma need additional resourcing while actively desensitizing memories in phase 4. With these clients, you will need to continue enhancing existing resources, creating new resources, and strengthening your therapeutic relationship, even if this means repeating or expanding on portions of previous phases. This is very different from sticking to a script or following along with an ordered set of phases; it requires attuning to your clients, no matter which phase they are currently in. This represents the difference between the traditional, linear model of EMDR and the holistic model I advocate for throughout this book.

This holistic model is especially important for clients who suffer from developmental and attachment trauma, for whom standard EMDR preparation strategies are not enough. In this case, it is helpful to use a method known as Constant Installation of Present Orientation and Safety (CIPOS; Knipe, 2018), which emphasizes the clients' orientation to the present moment while processing traumatic memories briefly. CIPOS helps to prevent clients from reexperiencing the trauma and can be especially helpful when working with trauma survivors who experience dissociation. For these clients in particular, preparation is not limited to phase 2, and in fact, may be needed throughout the entire process. And, as you will soon learn, preparation is not and should not be limited to the time spent in your office either.

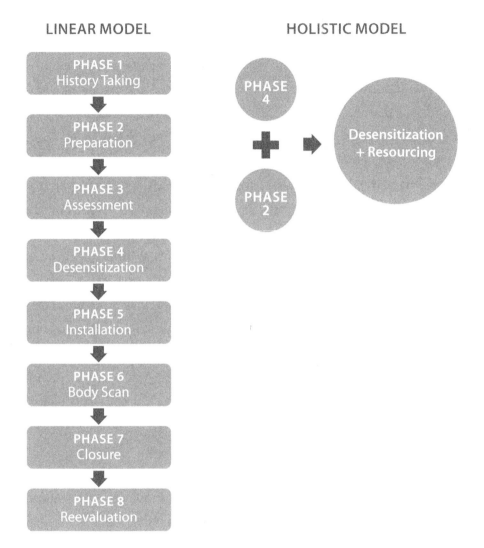

Preparation Doesn't End in Your Office

In chapter 1, I explored the brain's ability to rewire itself and create new neural pathways based on experience. It's important to understand that this capacity for neuroplasticity is strengthened with *repeated* use of *specific* neural networks. The application of this knowledge is especially relevant when it comes to resourcing your clients.

When clients practice new skills in your office, it's a great start, but if they don't keep practicing outside of the session, these skills are not going to be helpful in the long run. To permanently wire these skills into their brains, clients need to practice daily, between sessions, for an extended period of time. In this way, they will create new, more sustainable neural pathways.

The importance of between-session practice is illustrated by Pascual-Leone, the researcher I mentioned in chapter 1 who mapped the brains of individuals learning to read Braille. In his study, participants practiced Braille five days a week, Monday through Friday, for two hours a day. Their brains were mapped every Friday, at the end of each week, and every Monday, after taking a weekend break.

For the first six months of the study, Pascal-Leone found reverse neurological patterns between Friday's and Monday's brain mappings. On Fridays, he observed rapid changes in his subjects' brains, resulting from five days of practice, but by Monday, these changes reverted back to baseline, as if the subjects hadn't practiced at all. Interestingly, though, after the initial six months, these neurological patterns started to shift: On Fridays, the neural changes started to taper off, while on Mondays, he started seeing slow but noticeable changes. These neuroplastic changes highlight the difference between a *state* change and a *trait* change. The Friday brain mappings represented state change, or a temporary change in neurological patterns. The Monday brain mappings, on the other hand, were correlated with permanent neurological change, or what is known as trait change.

What does all this mean for your clients? The short answer is that practice results in long-term changes. You want clients to experience trait change, but this kind of change doesn't happen on its own. The ability to benefit from using skills in the long run is a result of regular and consistent practice. This is the only way for clients to achieve sustainable neural changes—trait changes—that will last long after they complete therapy. In the next chapter, I will talk about how to help clients create a structured practice that will allow them to achieve trait change. For now, let's continue our discussion on the practicality of preparing clients for processing, since solid preparation can make the difference between successful EMDR treatment and treatment with limited results.

Individualize Resources to Your Client's Needs

Galit was one of many clients who came to see me after having had a prior negative experience with EMDR. She had terminated treatment with her previous EMDR therapist before they even started processing because, as she explained, "My therapist kept insisting that I needed to put all my emotions in a box." Even though Galit felt this was an impossible task, her therapist insisted on using the container exercise in this inflexible way—the way it is taught in basic EMDR training. With no ability to think outside the box, she lost her client.

In basic EMDR training, you, too, may have learned that it is necessary to follow specific procedural scripts to have a successful preparation phase. Your trainer may have taught you that the container and the safe place exercises are required for every client, and that there are additional scripts you need to follow to successfully prepare your clients for processing. But what is more important is your flexibility and your focus on the present moment in the preparation phase. You need to customize the exercise to your clients' needs.

For example, consider the container exercise you learned in basic EMDR training as container 1.0. The traditional container exercise involves having clients place their emotions in a physical container, like a box, treasure chest, or bank vault, for temporary safekeeping. Some clients can use this version of the container exercise very effectively. But others, such as Galit, do not find it effective at all. For these clients, you will have to adopt a more creative approach and modify the traditional container exercise in innovative ways. Here are a few examples of how I have done so:

- **Container 2.0: Shipping the container.** Instead of just placing their emotions in a container, one of my clients used to put their container inside a FedEx truck that transported it to a secure underground shelter.

- **Container 3.0: Using advanced guided imagery.** When one of my clients struggled with the concept of a traditional container, we did a guided imagery exercise in which he turned his emotions and thoughts into a liquid, which was then poured into a secret pond only he had access to.

- **Container 4.0: Making it more abstract.** A client of mine with an infinite feeling of anger told me that no container in this world could hold all his anger, so we created containment that was outside of planet Earth. Together, we created an abstract container made out of a black hole, which was able to hold all his anger with the appropriate amount of gravity and energy.

- **Container 5.0: Making it more concrete.** Many of my clients, especially engineers and computer programmers, often conceptualize their thoughts and emotions as data, in a binary mode of bits and bytes. These clients may want to use a hard drive, a cloud drive, or sophisticated artificial intelligence algorithms as their container.

Don't limit the container exercise to your way of thinking or your knowledge. Even if you don't understand the gravity of black holes or artificial intelligence, it doesn't mean that using these methods won't work for your clients. Remember that any exercise or technique will be more effective once you customize it to your clients' needs and to their way of thinking. Let your *clients* decide what resources work for them. Unless these resources are contaminated.

Identify Contaminated Resources

The forms of usable resources are nearly limitless—in fact, they are as variable as your clients can make them—but among the possibilities are some that will not move your clients toward effective treatment. Contaminated resources are resources that have been linked with memories stored in maladaptive neural networks. Not only will using contaminated resources impede your clients' readiness for EMDR processing, but it has the potential to make things worse, so it's important that you and your clients identify contaminated resources from the get-go.

Many clients inadvertently use contaminated resources because they have *some* positive memories associated with certain places or people. For example, it is common for clients to have positive memories from a recent vacation, making it a great resource. But some clients experience tragic or unfortunate events while on vacation, such as losing their passport, missing a connecting flight, or coming down with a stomach bug, making this memory likely to trigger negative feelings and associations. Therefore, when selecting resources during the preparation phase, it's important to explain the concept of contaminated resources and emphasize why they should not be used. This will offer clients guidance in selecting resources that are helpful.

You must also be on the lookout for resources that become contaminated during the course of therapy. For example, one of my clients used her grandparents' house as her calm place, as she described having many positive memories there as both a child and an adult. But after her grandmother passed away, the house became the subject of a serious altercation between the client's mother and uncle, and the feelings of warmth and safety associated with this place became contaminated, so we had to develop a new calm place.

When you recognize that clients are using a contaminated resource, stop engaging in BLS and explore your options; it is possible to rework the existing resource, but in some cases, clients may need to choose an entirely new one. Here are a few suggestions from trauma and EMDR expert Laurel Parnell (2018), which I have extended and further developed based on my own clinical experience:

- **Use a container to store the negative memory.** If your client's original resource is contaminated because it is linked to a negative memory, try using a container to store the negative memory. Remember that the goal of the container exercise is to strengthen containment capacities, and each client should individualize their own container. If the client is able to successfully contain the negative memory, try using the existing resource with short BLS. If they can use the positive resource without the intrusion of any negative memories, gradually increase the length of the BLS sets.

- **Ask your client if they can think about a new resource.** While in session, have the client come up with a different resource that is associated with only positive memories. Remember that some clients need more support with replacing the contaminated resource with a new one. When needed, take the time to help them explore new resources.

- **Ask your client to create a new positive resource between sessions.** If clients have access to nature, they may try spending time by a mountain, a river, or any other place that is calm and feels safe. If this is not an option, they can use a place from a movie, a book, or the internet.

- **Have your client create an imaginary location.** For some clients, it feels safer to create a completely new place that is based solely on their imagination. Explore this option with clients as a way to create a helpful resource that is not linked to any existing memories.

Integrate Somatic Work into the Preparation Phase

When you start preparing your clients for EMDR processing, remember that you are not only helping them create resources. You are also getting them ready and orienting them for the work that follows—the processing phases. You want to make sure they understand how BLS works, including that slow BLS creates a calming effect, while fast BLS facilitates processing and will likely stimulate disturbing or traumatic memories from the past. In other words, you need to prepare your clients for the possibility that things will get intense.

If a client is not yet ready to experience high levels of disturbance, the processing phases may become ineffective, and their mental state can deteriorate, which can lead to early termination of therapy. To prevent this situation, use the preparation phase to introduce your clients to anything that may happen during the processing phases, including the likelihood of intense body sensations that may arise. This is something that many EMDR therapists fail to mention, as they often focus heavily on the thoughts and verbal expression associated with the target memory, minimizing the effects of the somatic experience. This is problematic, given that many clients—especially those with histories of developmental trauma—already have a tendency to avoid paying attention to bodily sensations. The preparation phase is an excellent opportunity to support these clients in developing somatic awareness and observing what they feel in their bodies, as these sensations will show up concurrently with thoughts and emotions during the processing phase.

The preparation phase is also an important time to help your clients develop the capacity for dual awareness so they can navigate any somatic discomfort or disturbing body sensations that may arise once they begin processing. With dual awareness, clients process disturbing memories by alternately focusing their attention on the source of the discomfort and then orienting themselves back to the safety of the present moment. You can help your clients practice dual awareness by asking them to notice the discomfort generated by a less disturbing recent memory followed by the positive effects on their minds and bodies that come as a result of using their resources. Dual awareness is necessary for successful EMDR treatment because it allows clients to incrementally confront traumatic memories without becoming overwhelmed.

Along with introducing the concept of dual awareness, here are a few additional suggestions to implement somatic work in the preparation phase (Schwartz & Maiberger, 2018):

- Containment of somatic distress. In this intervention, clients learn to use a container that is specifically designed to hold somatic distress and undesired bodily sensations. Encourage them to imagine their distressing bodily sensations as a color, which travels through their body and then exits so it can be stored inside the container. You can end this intervention with the light stream exercise, in which the client chooses a color associated with healing to replace the color associated with the somatic distress.

- **Affect and sensation tolerance.** Ask the client to focus on their breathing while you begin naming different emotions. Start with positive emotions, like joy and excitement, and then gradually move toward disturbing emotions, such as sadness, anger, and fear. This helps clients build tolerance to disturbing emotions and increases their capacity to regulate their emotions with their breath.

- **Postural awareness.** This intervention teaches clients to recognize the relationship between their thoughts, emotions, and posture. It allows them to see how their mental state can adaptively shift in response to certain body adjustments. To begin, ask your client to find a posture in which they feel grounded, and then add short sets of BLS to strengthen the positive state associated with this posture. This posture can later be used as a resource when processing trauma.

Integrate Breathwork into the Preparation Phase

If you pay close attention to your clients' breathing when they process targets in the desensitization phase, you will notice that, more often than not, they're holding their breath. In some cases, they'll hyperventilate. That's because when you activate the memory that was wired into the neural network, you're stimulating the breath pattern that occurred at the time of the traumatic event.

Whatever breath pattern a client is experiencing, your job is to help them notice and correct it. This can be practiced during the preparation phase by instructing your clients to slow down their breath with every set of BLS. When they do this repeatedly, they create a conditioned response between the BLS and a slower and deeper breath pattern. This practice will help them slow down their breathing during the desensitization phase, when their sympathetic nervous system becomes activated in response to the trauma memory. By guiding your clients to notice and slow down their breathing, you can help them reprogram some hardwired neurological patterns. In doing so, you help them reduce their physiological symptoms of anxiety, which are hardwired in their brainstem—deep inside the brain—where thoughts cannot be encoded.

Even if the client has not suffered from an explicit trauma, their nervous system is still likely to be on high alert in response to all the stressors of today's world. An absence of trauma does not equate to an absence of suffering. James Nestor (2020) explains this in *Breath: The New Science of a Lost Art*:

> It's much more common, especially in the modern world, to never experience full-blown, life-threatening stress, but to never fully relax either. We'll spend our days half-asleep and nights half-awake, lolling in a gray zone of half-anxiety. When we do, the vagus nerve stays half-stimulated. During these times, the organs throughout the body won't be "shut down," but will instead be half supported in a state of suspended animation: blood flow will decrease and communication between the organs and the brain will become choppy, like a conversation through a staticky phone line. Our bodies can persist like this for a while; they can keep us alive, but they can't keep us healthy. (p. 149)

So even if a client presents as relatively calm, the likelihood of them operating in a state of "half-anxiety" is high. Your clients are in your office because they want help to reduce their suffering. Anxiety comes with the territory. If you don't teach clients the skills to reduce anxiety, chances are the EMDR treatment won't be as effective.

How to Know When Your Client Is Ready to Start Processing

Remember that each client's readiness for processing is unique to them. Use the following list to assess your client's stability and determine if they are ready to start EMDR processing. These are general guidelines, so remember to use your clinical judgment when making a decision.

- **Do you have an established therapeutic relationship?** Does the client trust you? Do they feel safe and connected with you? Remember that trust is essential, since clients often find themselves in a very vulnerable state when processing trauma memories. How will you know if a client feels safe in your presence? They will tell you, and if they don't, simply ask them. Some clients with histories of childhood abuse and neglect need extended time to build rapport. In these cases, slower is better. Take as much time as you need to make sure that you and your client have a strong therapeutic relationship.

- **Can your client hold positive states?** If your client is able to effectively use the resourcing exercises after having practiced them in your office, this is a good sign. But if they are unable to hold adaptive material, processing is likely to be ineffective, and it won't lead to the desired outcomes. In that case, they need more preparation before you proceed. Continue helping them by fine-tuning existing resources or introducing them to additional resources.

- **Is your client able to maintain dual awareness?** Test your client's ability to keep one foot in the present and one foot in the past. Instead of starting with traumatic memories, you can start with a mildly disturbing incident that happened recently. Are they able to go back and forth between focusing on this incident and then returning their attention to the safety of the present? If they can't, they are not ready to process.

- **Does your client experience dissociation?** Clients who dissociate are at a higher risk of decompensation, but dissociation alone is not a contraindication for EMDR processing. It's not a matter of *if* they dissociate—we all do to some extent—it's a question of *how much*. Dissociation lies on a continuum, ranging from normal experiences of daydreaming or "spacing out" to the more intense experiences of derealization and identity confusion, so some clients may be able to successfully process EMDR targets if they dissociate, depending on their capacity to maintain dual awareness. What makes the difference between "adaptive" dissociation and "maladaptive" dissociation is the client's awareness of the dissociative process and their ability to bring themselves back to the present. In EMDR, you always want to avoid maladaptive dissociation and detect it when it happens.

- **Is your client able to tolerate intense body sensations?** When your client begins processing trauma, they will experience a lot of emotional intensity in their body. If somatic memories arise, make sure they are able to regulate with their breath or by using other somatic interventions. For examples of somatic interventions, see "Phase 6: Body Scan Done Better" in chapter 7.

- **Is there a current crisis in your client's life?** Clients who experience substantial crises may not be able to process disturbing material. For example, a client who recently lost their job and cannot afford therapy may not be a good candidate for EMDR processing that would potentially take a long time. Similarly, clients who have unstable living environments, such as domestic violence or drug use, are often not ready to start EMDR processing. If you recognize that transitioning to processing is not clinically appropriate, do what you can to support and resource your client. Hopefully, by the time the crisis is over, they will be ready to start processing.

- **Is your client at risk of harming themselves or others?** Make sure clients with suicidal or homicidal ideation are stabilized before beginning EMDR processing. When clients express suicidal or homicidal ideation, focus on their safety before attempting any EMDR work. Create a safety plan that includes limited access to firearms, specify who they would call if their disturbing ideations intensify, and agree on a concrete plan to ensure their (and others') safety.

- **Is there a pending legal case?** Active legal involvement does not always prevent clients from starting processing, but it should be taken into consideration. Will successful processing have the potential to affect any legal cases? Will it affect your client's testimony? Educate the client and, if necessary, talk with their attorney about any potential consequences that EMDR may have on the client's legal case.

- **Are there any health concerns?** If your client has health conditions that may be worsened by EMDR processing (e.g., heart disease or certain neurological issues), consult with their medical providers.

- **Are there any secondary gains or losses?** Clients who identify with their symptoms may be afraid of getting better since successful processing will lead to some loss. Moreover, clients who improve in treatment can also lose tangible things, such as government benefits or peer support. If you identify any secondary gains and losses, make sure to discuss them with your client. Sometimes talk therapy is necessary to address these issues before starting EMDR. A motivational interviewing approach can help clients who are ambivalent about moving forward with treatment.

- **Is your client afraid to start EMDR processing?** Some clients have fears about starting EMDR processing. This fear can arise from past unsuccessful EMDR treatment or from a client's inability to trust themselves with intense emotions. Even if you believe that your client is ready, never push them to start processing if *they* don't feel ready. Instead, help them address these fears with further education and more resourcing.

- **Is your client pressuring you to start processing?** On the other hand, never let your client pressure you into starting processing before *you* feel they are ready. Trust your clinical judgment about your client's readiness for processing, and don't let the client alone decide when to start.

- **Did your client experience repeated attachment wounds in childhood?** Standard EMDR preparation strategies, like the container and safe place exercises, may not be enough for clients with attachment wounds and developmental trauma. For these clients, it may be necessary to supplement EMDR with the developmental needs meeting strategy (DNMS), which was created by Shirley Jean Schmidt. DNMS calls for you to assess the nature and severity of attachment wounds and identify issues connected to child parts who may need stabilization before identifying the target memories for processing. You can find more information about DNMS in Schmidt's (2020) book, *Ego State Therapy Interventions to Prepare Attachment-Wounded Adults for EMDR.*

Finally, one of the most effective ways to prepare your clients for processing is to introduce them to the power of mindfulness skills, which can help them process better in session and improve their ability to regulate their emotions in and out of session. In the next chapter, I'll provide you with some psychoeducation on the benefits of mindfulness and introduce some tools and tips to help your clients (and yourself) develop a routine meditation practice.

CHAPTER 5

EMDR and Mindfulness

· ·

*We do believe there is an art to practicing EMDR that
can be cultivated by recognizing the similarities between
mindfulness practices and EMDR therapy.*

—Jamie Marich and Stephen Dansiger,
EMDR Therapy and Mindfulness for Trauma-Focused Care

· · · · · · · · · · · · · · · · · · · ·

No doubt you've heard the word *mindfulness.* It's on your social media feeds, in all the wellness literature, and even on the curriculum of some kindergarten classrooms. Everybody seems to be doing it, or at least discussing its merits. But do you *really* know what mindfulness is all about? Moreover, why should you care?

There are two reasons to consider mindfulness in the context of your EMDR work:

1. A mindfulness practice will, hands down, make you a better EMDR therapist.

2. Teaching your clients mindfulness, and supporting them in making it a practice, will make their EMDR therapy work more quickly and more effectively.

When you incorporate mindfulness into your therapy practice, you are more present for your clients, your clients are more present for their therapy, and you both come out feeling calmer and healthier. Therefore, in addition to covering the origins and theory behind the practice of mindfulness, this chapter discusses the most relevant research in the field, teaches you how to integrate mindfulness into your EMDR work, and shares some tools and resources to help with creating a meditation routine. Even if you think you already know everything about mindfulness and its myriad benefits, don't skip this chapter.

Life is busy, but it's important that you don't neglect your own mindfulness practice because you "don't have time." The truth is that mindfulness practices are free, require no equipment or special setting, and can be done in less time than you spend scrolling through your social media accounts. In order to become a better clinician, you need to prioritize this practice. So, if you are invested in your professional growth but can't find the time for mindfulness, let's change that.

What Is Mindfulness?

Let's begin by making sure we're on the same page with our understanding of this trending term. Dan Harris (2017), author of *Meditation for Fidgety Skeptics*, defines mindfulness as "the ability to see what's happening in your head at any given moment, so that you don't get carried away by it" (p. 12). Another author, and the pioneer of mindfulness-based stress reduction, Jon Kabat-Zinn (2005), defines it as "paying attention in a particular way: on purpose, in the present moment, and nonjudgmentally" (p. 4).

In other words, mindfulness is the ability to stay present and notice what's in front of you. Throughout this chapter, I will use the terms *mindfulness* and *meditation* interchangeably, though there are slight differences between the two. Meditation is a formal practice of mindfulness, such as sitting and observing the breath, whereas mindfulness can be done informally throughout your day, without the need to engage in a specific activity. More than a technique, mindfulness is a way of being. Mindfulness can be done when you meditate, when you wash the dishes, or when you take a shower. Mindfulness can even be practiced when you work, especially if you're a therapist.

The word *mindfulness* is a translation of the Pali word *sati*, which means "awareness." The practice of mindfulness is believed to originate from the Buddha's teachings more than 2,500 years ago. These teachings then made their way to the Western world in the 1960s and have since grown in popularity. Since then, we have adapted mindfulness to fit our busy lives and given it our own spin—and in the process, lost some of the context of what the Buddha was trying to teach us. We turned mindfulness into McMindfulness—in other words, the practice has become monopolized by mindfulness programs, classes, and apps.

Mindfulness was not developed as a set of evidence-based techniques but as a way of being. The Buddha didn't have a YouTube channel or a podcast, and he never used apps to meditate. Therefore, before you download the popular Headspace app, let's discuss how you can be most successful while being mindful.

Your Brain on Mindfulness

Many therapists need a practice to be "evidence-based" to believe that it works. Fortunately, with the advancements in brain imaging that have been made available over the last decades, research has shown—and continues to prove—the neural evidence base of mindfulness. What used to be considered an esoteric practice done by non-Westerners and "hippies" is now being researched in prestigious academic institutions and neuroscience labs all over the world. The ability to look inside the brain and see the neuronal changes that occur as a result of mindfulness has taken the mystical aspects of this practice and made it more concrete and commonplace.

While this brain imaging research has made mindfulness more desirable to the masses, especially those who would have not otherwise considered engaging in a "spiritual" practice, it has come with a cost: Many people expect to see gains with very minimal effort. With mindfulness, though, gains are made *with time* and *over time*—that is, by practicing for longer periods of time in one sitting (in minutes) and by practicing over an extended period (in years). So what is the difference between a deep mindfulness practice, as done by dedicated mindfulness practitioners, and the practice that most of us are doing? Let's take a closer look.

Deep versus Wide: Making Mindfulness More Accessible

In Daniel Goleman and Richard Davidson's (2018) book, *Altered Traits: Science Reveals How Meditation Changes Your Mind, Brain, and Body*, the authors distinguish between two approaches to mindfulness: the deep and the wide. The deep approach is the most intensive, requiring many hours of individual practice, while the wide approach makes mindfulness more accessible—and much less time-consuming—through easy-to-use apps. In order to understand the differences between the deep and the wide, consider these three groups of meditators:

- **Beginner meditators.** These individuals typically have fewer than 100 hours of practice. This group includes clients who meditate three times a week with an app for no more than ten minutes. Most of us are in this group.

- **Long-term meditators.** These practitioners have somewhere between 1,000 and 10,000 hours of practice. They typically attend meditation retreats and, in many cases, have a regular meditation practice.

- **The yogis.** These are the "elite athletes" of meditators. They have meditated for tens of thousands of hours. The average number of meditation hours for this group is around 27,000. These people are solidly in the deep group.

The effects of meditation (as measured by neural firing patterns in the brain) are variable across each of these three groups, suggesting that the benefits of mindfulness are strongly correlated with the number of hours that an individual has been practicing.

Why might this be? You already know the answer: neuroplasticity. The same neuroplastic rules we've discussed in previous chapters apply to mindfulness.

Research shows that yogis have elevated gamma oscillations, which is a type of firing pattern that most of us experience for split seconds at most (Goleman & Davidson, 2018). Elevated gamma is characterized by a high quality of awareness and the ability to be fully present. As opposed to most of us who experience this state for a second at a time or less, the most experienced meditators hold this mental state for minutes. What's more, this distinct neural activity is not only seen when yogis actively meditate but also as they go about their daily activity. Their brains have literally been restructured due to the number of hours they've spent meditating. In other words, yogis have achieved altered *traits* as opposed to altered *states*, which is what most beginner meditators experience as a result of a few minutes of meditation practice.

Most of your clients likely don't have a spare 27,000 hours to get deep into the practice of meditation. The good news is that you don't need to send them to an ashram in India for them to experience trait change. Remember the Braille study from chapter 1? You'll need to help your clients do exactly what the Braille learners did: engage in daily practice for an extended period of time. In other words, to see real change, your clients will have to spend some time meditating while observing their breath and their thoughts. And they will have to do it regularly and consistently—every day for several months.

While this may seem daunting, remind your clients that most of them already participate in some form of consistent daily practice—for instance, practicing good oral hygiene by brushing their teeth twice a day. Think of mindfulness meditation as good hygiene for the mind. And just as tooth brushing has become a nearly automatic habit, the practice of meditation can develop the same way. While your clients may never show the same neural patterns as the yogis, it will improve their emotion regulation abilities and help them better process their EMDR targets.

With that in mind, let's discuss the first step to cultivating any mindfulness practice: becoming the observer.

Welcome the Observer

You'll recall from chapter 1 that we all have a default mode network, or DMN, that helps us operate on autopilot. It's just the way our brains are wired. When we run on autopilot, we are more efficient and don't have to spend energy thinking about the hundreds of routines we enact every day. But efficiency has a price. When someone is always living their life in autopilot, their brain can get stuck—not just in terms of their actions but also in terms of their thoughts and emotions. Many clients enter therapy because they suffer from inflexible thought patterns that they are unable to change. Worse yet, many clients start believing the narrative of these thoughts.

In meditation and in EMDR, your role as a therapist is to help your clients see that there is another way to relate to their experiences. You teach them to observe raw sensory data (what they hear, see, smell, taste, and feel) for what it is—just data—so they can view things as they are, without distortions. By developing the ability to look at their reality more objectively, and creating distance from the meaning they have assigned to events, your clients will start to see the world more objectively. They change from autopilot mode to observer mode. They become *observers.*

The Buddha called the experience of observing raw sensory data "emptiness" or "formlessness." Mindfulness practices can help clients get a little taste of formlessness. In a state of deep mindfulness, they don't attempt to stop or push away their thoughts, feelings, or body sensations. Instead, they observe them without assigning them any meaning.

This ability to sit and observe incoming sensory data is not something that comes naturally to most clients, but it improves significantly with regular practice. Remind your clients that meditation enhances the effects of EMDR, which can lead to dramatic improvements in their lives. However, you do need to set realistic expectations: EMDR is not the path to nirvana. It can resolve a lot of the pain your clients are feeling, but it won't completely remove all the suffering.

Aiming for Adaptive Resolution versus Nirvana

In *Awakening the Buddha Within: Eight Steps to Enlightenment*, author Lama Surya Das (1998) notes, "Achieving freedom from craving and being in the world, yet not quite *of* it, is up to us; achieving liberation, lasting happiness, and freedom is up to us" (p. 86). Reading these words, you might think that liberation is right around the corner. That if you meditate, you will achieve liberation from all the suffering in this world. You may be tempted to convince your clients that freedom from suffering is a few breaths away.

While I appreciate the optimism, true liberation—*nirvana*—is not likely on any of your clients' lists of treatment goals. When people achieve nirvana (and some people actually do!), they live a truly objective life, without the distortions most of us experience. These enlightened beings live their lives in a state of observation. They are mindful of their own distortions for most of the time. This is a really great way to live, but it's something most of us can't achieve.

Still, some clients, and even some therapists, have the idea that EMDR will end all of their suffering. This can lead to a lot of disappointment because EMDR treatment, even when done very effectively, does not remove the suffering from your clients' lives. It doesn't remove what the Buddha called *dukkha*, most accurately translated as "dissatisfaction." Our tendency in life is to be unsatisfied, which often leads to suffering.

For many people, suffering meant seeing Donald Trump on their phones and computer screens every day—and sometimes in their bad dreams—for four years. I think that even the monks with elevated gamma oscillations would be a little agitated if they had to deal with him every day.

But dissatisfaction with certain people is just one form of suffering. The Buddha taught us that wanting or craving also leads to suffering. This means that even if you help clients heal the wounds of the past, they will still experience suffering from the cravings they have in life. Your clients will still want delicious ice cream, a new car, the latest iPhone, a Peloton® bike, and so on. These are all great things to have, but this desire to always have more causes your clients to maintain dukkha.

Therefore, you'll want to set clear expectations about what therapy and EMDR treatment in particular can do for them. Your clients should know the difference between nirvana, which is not likely to occur as a result of any therapy, and adaptive resolution, which is the goal of EMDR. (Though if many of your clients actually achieve nirvana, please shoot me an email; I want you to be my new therapist ☺.) Life should get a lot better after successful EMDR therapy, but it will not be free from suffering. Your clients will still have to grapple with the painful existence of climate change, White supremacy, gun violence, and many other things.

How to Develop Right View

For clients to get the most out of their mindfulness practices, they have to understand *why* they need to meditate. They have to learn about *right view*, which is a concept that starts with the eightfold path. A popular analogy used in Tibetan Buddhism is that a person who meditates without knowing the purpose of meditation is like a blind man walking around without any sense of direction. So let's dive a little deeper.

According to the teachings of the Buddha, some of our suffering results from having the wrong perception of the world. When we see things from our own perspective, our distortions prevent us from seeing things objectively. The Buddha reminds us that with *right view*, or by removing the "I" from our perspective, we can see reality as it is. Seeing the world with right view is needed for the development of *prajna*—"wisdom" in Sanskrit.

You can teach your clients about right view when they start EMDR and the practice of mindfulness. A great entry point to this lesson is when clients say, "I am not doing it right"—about either EMDR or meditation. To teach your clients right view, explore with them the subjective experience of "not doing it right" and remind them that there is no right way to do these things. The subjective experience of not doing something right often stems from clients' core beliefs about themselves, such as the belief that they are flawed, inadequate, or less-than in some way. Make sure to explore these beliefs and help your clients understand that they don't represent absolute reality. Instead, they often reflect distorted ways of viewing and interpreting the world. This understanding can help them start seeing reality as it is, with more objectivity.

However, for many clients, seeing things objectively is not familiar territory because they suffer from *blocking beliefs*. The Buddha called these beliefs "delusions" and explained that they are formed by a process of conditioning. Your clients see the world from their own narrow perspective because of what happened to them in the past, and when it comes to trauma, these self-referential beliefs tend to be rigid. Take, for example, a client who was abandoned by their biological parents and neglected by their adoptive parents. This individual develops the core belief "I'm unlovable" and continues to hold it throughout adulthood, despite having evidence to the contrary. This client is unable to look at the data in front of them (e.g., having a loving spouse and friends who care about them) and instead restricts their view to their early childhood experiences.

Blocking beliefs can't be removed by just telling clients to "notice" them and apply BLS because these beliefs have been so deeply encoded in their neural networks. Instead, these beliefs are more likely to change if your clients understand right view because it teaches them to remove "I" and observe the difference between what happened *then* and what is happening *now*. For example, returning to the client who was abandoned and neglected by their parents, implementing right view can help them shift their core beliefs by observing what is happening in front of them. By observing the data, they learn not to believe everything they thought was true. They learn not to identify with their own blocking beliefs.

This process of removing themselves from the situation helps clients see reality with more objectivity. Remember that the art and science of EMDR is not limited to just repeating a script or a protocol. The magic of EMDR happens when clients process past events with more objectivity—with right view. This can only happen with full presence—with attention to the here and now. That's how perspective is changed.

But perspective alone isn't sufficient for your clients to achieve their goals. As you probably already know, many people struggle to develop a regular mindfulness practice. They may start and stop, or they might find it hard to stay consistent. To help your clients develop a regular practice, you must guide them. This represents the next step of the eightfold path, *right action*, which helps clients implement an evidence-based system of building habits.

Taking Right Action

After clients come to understand the rationale for mindfulness by developing right view, they will be more motivated to take *right action*. That said, many clients may understand and even practice right view but continue to struggle with developing a formal meditation practice. Why? Because developing a new habit is hard.

The most effective way to help your clients develop a regular meditation practice is to understand the science of habit formation and the three conditions that are necessary for a habit to form: cues, routines, and rewards (Duhigg, 2014). Learning how to manipulate cues and rewards will allow you to work with clients to implement a daily meditation routine

until it becomes a habit. And if meditation is not already a part of *your* routine, implementing your own daily practice should become a priority.

Here are a few tips for helping your clients create a regular practice:

- **Tie the habit to a repeating cue.** Encourage your clients to schedule meditation around a daily task or at a certain time of day. For example, the cue can be tied to an event, such as their morning shower, lunchtime break, or bedtime routine, or it can involve a daily alarm that sounds at 8 p.m. Have your clients do whatever works for them, as long as they stay consistent with these cues.

- **Start with 5–10 minutes.** Tell your clients that 5–10 minutes will not be enough in the long run, but that it's a very good way to start developing a habit. If they want to spend more time meditating, they are more than welcome.

- **Use apps when starting out.** Meditation apps are exceptionally good at helping people develop a habit. Most of these apps can even help with cues, timing, or recording streaks of performance, but be sure that clients understand that they shouldn't depend on apps in the long run.

- **Meditation devices can help.** Similar to apps, meditation devices can be an excellent tool for creating a new habit—though like apps, clients shouldn't depend on these in the long run. I let my clients borrow a Muse™, which is an electroencephalogram headband that can read brain waves and provide real-time feedback while the client is meditating. If the client is "in the zone," they will hear a quiet bird sound—a little reward to motivate their brain to continue the same neural activity. If they start ruminating, Muse will increase a background sound to remind the client that they are off track. This can be very helpful for clients who have just started meditating and are getting lost in their thoughts. Other forms of meditation devices may include equipment like virtual reality headsets.

- **Start with the right type of meditation.** There are numerous types of meditation. While some, like breath work, have better long-term benefits, they can be difficult to stick with at the outset. Your task is to help your clients find the right fit, especially for habit formation. The type of meditation can always change later, once the habit is formed.

So which types of meditation should you and your clients choose from? To answer this question, let's turn to Jeff Tarrant (2017), a pioneer in the study of *neuromeditation*, which is the application of brain-based principles to meditative practices. Tarrant has done fascinating work measuring the brain activity of people using different types of meditation. He describes his four favorite styles of neuromeditation:

1. **Focus.** Also known as *concentration meditation*, this is the type of meditation in which you focus on the breath. Many therapists teach this type first. While the long-term benefits of breath work are clear, this practice can temporarily lead to an increase in rumination, which can be a very unpleasant experience, especially for clients who suffer from anxiety, depression, or trauma. See "Simple Mindful Breath Meditation" at the end of this chapter for instructions on this technique.

2. **Mindfulness.** In this type of meditation, clients bring an awareness to their present-moment experience. Here, clients assume an open and nonjudgmental attitude as they turn their attention to any thoughts, emotions, or sensations as they arise. This meditation can be incorporated into your therapy sessions and can be helpful for individuals with ADHD, addictions and cravings, anxiety, and chronic stress.

3. **Quiet mind.** This type of meditation involves focusing on mantras or moving from sustained attention to silence. Mantras used can be words or phrases taken from any spiritual or religious tradition that have some personal meaning to your clients. Mantras can range from simple repetitions of the word *om* to any motivational statements that help clients feel more relaxed or inspired (e.g., "Breathing in, I am calm. Breathing out, I am safe"). Individuals who practice this type of meditation report a "relaxed spacious awareness" (Tarrant, 2017, p. 115), which correlates with lower activity in the DMN. This meditation can

work well for clients who have a rigid view of themselves and need help with increasing cognitive flexibility.

4. **Open heart, loving-kindness, or compassion.** This style of meditation involves the activation of positive feelings. Compassion meditation is a regular practice for yogis, but your clients don't have to be an "elite athlete" of meditation to benefit from this technique. In fact, if they struggle with developing a regular meditation practice, or if sitting with their thoughts while trying to observe their breath is too overwhelming, compassion meditation is a good practice to start with. You can find several practices and exercises in Christopher Germer and Kristin Neff's (2018) *The Mindful Self-Compassion Workbook*, which also comes with recordings of exercises that clients can listen to and then practice.

The Mindful Therapist

If you haven't read Jamie Marich and Stephen Dansiger's (2017) *EMDR Therapy and Mindfulness for Trauma-Focused Care*, please get a copy. In it, they explain how a mindful therapist is a better therapist. A mindful therapist can stay present when their clients abreact and dissociate. A mindful therapist can also maintain awareness when clients trigger something in them. Without this ability to maintain awareness and be in observer mode, you can't model a different way of being to your clients. You can't take your clients with you to the observer seat and teach them to "just notice."

In addition, if you're not mindful—if you don't stay in the observer seat—EMDR can negatively affect you and even lead to burnout. If you're like most dedicated EMDR therapists, you are exhausted by the end of your workday. That happens because you're doing a good job. Doing EMDR is some of the most rewarding work you can do, but it can be draining. By helping your clients create a different relationship with their emotions, you sometimes absorb some of these emotions. Sometimes your body feels what your clients are feeling in their bodies.

Therefore, it's also important to take self-care very seriously. This requires more than meditating between clients or taking a yoga class once a week. Effective self-care requires us to be proactive by cultivating a regular mindfulness practice. Many people struggle with keeping their meditation practice consistent over a long period of time. They start and they stop. They feel like life is too busy. But developing a daily practice is essential, even if you have kids and you're always busy—especially if you have kids and you're always busy. If you don't already have a meditation practice, use the tips in this chapter to begin.

With that in mind, let me end with a quote from *EMDR Therapy and Mindfulness for Trauma-Focused Care*: "For EMDR therapists specifically, consider that without mindfulness practices, EMDR therapy may in fact be incomplete, as is our ability to be ambassadors for this call to thrive" (Marich & Dansiger, 2017, p. 150).

Simple Mindful Breath Meditation

This mindful breath meditation is simple: All you have to do is breathe and pay attention to the air that goes in and out of your nose. Whenever you notice a thought, gently bring the attention back to the breath. That's all. Do it over and over again. A hundred times, a thousand times, a million times. Notice and shift the attention to the breath. This practice is simple, but it's not easy.

To help your clients cultivate this practice, you can use the following script or visit https://emdartnscience.com/book for a guided audio version. I encourage you to start with as little as 5 minutes a day and build to 20 minutes or longer.

1. Start in a comfortable position in which your body feels supported. You may be seated, reclined, lying on your back, or in any position that gives you ease. Place your hands wherever they feel comfortable, perhaps out to the sides or over your heart. Close your eyes or keep them open with a soft, gentle focus.

2. Take a few slow, easy breaths. *[Pause.]*

3. As you breathe, notice any tension in your body. See if you can release the tension with every exhale. *[Pause.]*

4. Notice how your body feels as you gently breathe in and out. *[Pause.]*

5. Notice how your breath moves you. Notice your chest and belly rise and fall. Perhaps feel the air as it enters and exits your nostrils. Simply notice. *[Pause.]*

6. Your mind may start to wander. Thoughts may clamor for your attention. Simply acknowledge your thoughts and then return your focus to your breath. *[Pause.]*

7. Begin to notice the wise rhythm of your breath, flowing in and out, in and out, without effort. *[Pause.]*

8. When thoughts return, acknowledge them. Try not to give them attention. Just notice them. Allow them to come and go just like your breath. *[Pause.]* Keep returning to your breath, in and out. *[Pause for several minutes.]*

9. Slowly bring your attention to the room. Gently blink your eyes open if they are closed. Take in your surroundings. Silently express gratitude for the simple beauty of your breath.

CHAPTER 6

Setting the Ground for Effective Processing

. . . .

EMDR therapy is a nonlinear process—you know where you want to go, but you don't know exactly how you'll get there.

—Michael Baldwin and Deborah Korn,
Every Memory Deserves Respect

. . . .

With each and every EMDR client you work with, you have one shared goal: to guide them on the path to adaptive resolution. The journey to reaching this goal is different for every client, but it requires you to know how to effectively process target memories. But before you can do that, you need some preparation. This is not another preparation phase for your clients but, rather a preparation for *you*. It is about enhancing your own readiness to begin processing work with clients. Therefore, in this chapter, I'll continue the discussion on how to approach EMDR more holistically and teach you how to:

- Bring your authentic self as an EMDR therapist

- Stay in control of the protocol

- Structure your sessions

- Use the expectancy effect to improve treatment outcomes

- Bring more flexibility and fluidity to phase 3 (assessment)

- Approach clusters using a nonlinear approach

These tools will help you become a more confident and creative EMDR therapist.

Be Your Authentic Self

Most therapists fresh out of basic EMDR training believe they are doing the right thing by reciting the standard protocol to their clients word for word. After all, this is what they have been taught to do. But if you get caught up in reading the protocol verbatim, you can come across as a robot and lose your sense of authenticity. Reading a script in a monotone voice is not going to make your clients feel confident in your abilities. Your clients need to trust that you know what you are doing. In my experience, memorizing the protocol is a better idea. When you have it memorized, you will come across as more confident and authentic during the processing phases and, in turn, your clients will feel more at ease.

Here are a few additional points to help you bring your authentic self when processing:

- **Be aware of your nonverbals.** When you set up a target memory, be mindful of your tone of voice and how attentive you are to your clients. Make sure you also sound like yourself—if you don't, they will lose confidence.

- **Listen to your clients.** In chapter 3, I emphasized the importance of letting clients talk. And when they talk, you need to listen. If your clients feel the need to tell you more than you asked about, don't cut them short. Listen with curiosity and interest.

- **Be flexible.** In Parnell's (2006) book, *A Therapist's Guide to EMDR*, she recommends not worrying about the order of information when setting up the target. Instead, she suggests allowing clients to organically describe their experience and take in the necessary information as it unfolds. For example, if you ask about cognitions, and a client needs to discuss their emotions and body sensations before they can recognize the negative cognition, take Parnell's suggestion—write it down and move on.

Stay in Control of the Protocol

Another reason I advocate for memorizing the standard protocol, instead of reading it verbatim, is because when you fixate on reading every single word on the page, you're not fully able to attune to your clients' ever-changing needs. You miss out on important nonverbal cues and shifts in energy if your eyes are focused on reading the sheet in front of you. You give up some of your control over the process. Therefore, it's important to take the time to properly conceptualize the protocol instead of always reciting it verbatim.

To illustrate this point, consider Yaniv, who was one of my first EMDR clients. A man in his midthirties, he came to me to treat his severe social anxiety. In the history-taking phase, we identified some of the target memories that stemmed from multiple incidents in childhood in which he was embarrassed by his alcoholic father. As an adult, it was extremely hard for him to be around people, especially women.

After we established rapport and developed some resources, we moved on to the assessment phase. I asked Yaniv, "What picture represents the worst part of the incident?" and then "When you bring up this picture, what negative belief do you have about yourself?" I made sure to read out the questions verbatim. However, in doing so, I stopped paying attention to subtle changes in Yaniv's emotions. I didn't pick up on his changing facial expression. I didn't realize he was holding his breath. By prioritizing the reading of the words, I lost my ability to be attuned to my client and lost control of the protocol.

Yaniv and I never got to do phase 4 because this was our last session. He never came back to see me. This was an early lesson that led me to the realization that I needed to know the protocol better so I could focus on my client, rather than the protocol.

In order to feel in control of the EMDR protocol, you need to practice with flow and be more intuitive. Flow and intuition don't come naturally and require some preparation. Therefore, before you start a session with a client who is ready to start desensitizing target memories (phase 4), and is already done with the assessment phase (phase 3), consider going through the following steps.

1. Have the standard protocol in front of you. Read it one step at a time, slowly.

2. Bring to mind a target that you need to process with your client.

3. Write down the four core components of the target memory: image, negative cognition, emotion, and sensation. For now, don't worry about the validity of cognition (VOC), subjective unit of disturbance (SUD), or positive cognition (PC).

4. When you have it all written down, take a moment to visualize the four core components of the target.

5. Without looking at the sheet, ask yourself again: What is the *image* (or other sense), what is the *negative cognition*, what *emotions* came up for your client, and what were their *body sensations*?

6. If you don't immediately remember one of the target memory components, take a minute. Don't immediately look at the sheet in front of you. Try to properly conceptualize the target, as it will help you better understand your client's experience.

7. If you're still unable to recall what's missing, think about what you visualized in step 4. Are you missing an image, a cognition, an emotion, or a sensation?

8. Go back to your sheet, look at what you wrote down, and compare your mental notes with your written notes. Think about your client's experience. How did they feel? What was it like for them to experience these emotions and these body sensations? How did this memory lead to the development of a negative self-belief that they hold to this day (their negative cognition)?

These steps will help you slow down and understand your client's experience by thinking about each of the four core components of the target memory that you need to remember: image, cognition, emotions, and body sensations. As you will soon learn, the other three parts of the standard protocol—the SUD, VOC, and PC—can wait or, in some cases, may be omitted.

Structure Your Sessions

One of the most common problems that beginner EMDR therapists run into is not structuring the EMDR session. If your client spends the first 30 minutes of the session telling you about their week, you will not have enough time for processing. Make sure you allow enough time for processing and for adequately closing the session. Here are some tips on how to structure an EMDR session:

- Set the intentions at the beginning of the session by asking your client, "Are we doing EMDR today?"

- Agree on a specific time for check-in (usually 5–10 minutes for a 50-minute session).

- Schedule a longer session, if appropriate. Longer sessions can be 90 minutes, 2 hours, or longer, depending on the client's current needs, availability, or financial situation.

- Consider scheduling more than one session per week. This will allow you to dedicate one session to EMDR and still have another one for talking with your client about weekly issues or using it as an integration session.

- Make sure you allow enough time to end the session properly. Especially when working with clients who have complex trauma, give yourself enough time to conclude the session with some emotion regulation strategies or any other technique that will help your client leave the session regulated.

Use the Expectancy Effect to Improve Treatment Outcomes

The expectancy effect is a phenomenon that is most commonly described in the context of distorted research results. When researchers expect certain outcomes, they unconsciously influence the subjects who participate in the study, and as a result, the outcomes of the study are skewed by the researchers' expectations. In research, distorting results in this way is problematic. In EMDR, however, you can use the power of the expectancy effect to your advantage by deliberately influencing treatment outcomes. Let me explain.

In basic EMDR training, you learned that educating clients on how EMDR works is part of the preparation phase. But if you want to use the expectancy effect to improve treatment outcomes, you have to keep educating your clients (and yourself) about EMDR throughout treatment. By continuing the discussion, you enhance your clients' expectations that EMDR will work for them. You can think of the expectancy effect as an enhancement of the placebo effect. It might feel like cheating, but if it helps your clients in the long run, who cares? Keep talking with your clients about how EMDR works, how it works *for them*, and the changes they will experience as a result of processing.

This is a strategy that wasn't mentioned in any training I have taken or by any of my EMDR consultants. However, once I started using the expectancy effect, it became a game changer in my EMDR work, and I observed significant improvements in my clients' treatment outcomes.

For example, Dana came to see me for trauma she had suffered throughout her childhood. After a few months of preparation and rapport building, we started processing a traumatic memory she had from age seven. At the end of the session, her SUD level went from 10 to 1. The target was not completed, but we were definitely moving in the right direction.

A week later, Dana told me that after our last processing session, she was "in an elated state" for the rest of the day. She was able to feel a sense of calm she had never experienced before. We used the session to enhance that feeling with slow BLS, and I explained that her brain was changing as a result of our work. We talked about the principles of neuroplasticity and neural integration, and I described how her traumatic memory was now getting information from different parts of her brain—information that was not accessible before.

Dana was grateful and said she could feel how her brain was changing. She was able to notice the flow of information inside her brain and how her negative cognition ("I am stuck") changed as a result of these neural changes. By continuing to talk about how EMDR works, and how it was working for her, I used the expectancy effect to enhance Dana's therapy outcome.

Bring More Flexibility and Fluidity to Phase 3

Successful EMDR treatment requires finding the right targets and the right components for each target. In phase 3 (assessment), you will do just that. Remember that there are four core components for each target:

1. Image (or another sense)

2. Negative cognition

3. Emotions

4. Body sensations

In this section, you will learn how to identify these four components, as well as the three other components (PC, VOC, and SUD), and brainstorm how to manage common issues that often come up during the assessment phase. I will discuss some solutions to potential problems, including how to be creative when you don't get the answers you are expecting from your clients.

Finding the Target Components

In order to effectively process EMDR targets, you have to find the right target components. Working with the wrong target components is like using the wrong ingredients when following a recipe: Your desired outcome is going to be compromised and you'll end up with a big mess. During the assessment phase, make sure you spend as much time as you need finding the right target components. Let's begin by getting you familiarized with each target component.

Target Component 1: The Image

The first component of a target is the image most closely associated with the traumatic memory. For some clients, the image of the most disturbing part of their memory is very clear—they know exactly what it is. For others, however, finding an image is not an easy task. If you ask a client about the worst image associated with their disturbing memory and they don't have one, know that the image doesn't have to be an image at all; it can be any sensory detail associated with the trauma.

For example, war veterans often report that the smell of burned flesh is more dominant than visual images, and people who have been involved in car accidents often say that the sound of the crash left a stronger imprint than any visual image. Many survivors of childhood sexual abuse also don't have a visual image of their trauma because the abuse happened in the dark, but the smell of alcohol from their abuser is often strongly associated with the disturbing memory. Therefore, if clients connect a different sense with their traumatic memory, use it to replace the visual image or add another sense as needed. You want to use whichever sense was wired into their maladaptive neural network at the time of the trauma.

For example, Shimshon was a male in his forties who suffered from depression and loneliness his whole life. His parents, both alcoholics, had never given any attention to his emotional state and often left him alone in the house while partying with their friends. In turn, Shimshon learned not to talk about his emotions. He had no friends and felt that the members of the rock band The Cure were the only people who could understand him and the depths of his sadness. Because of this, he listened to The Cure thousands of times during his teenage years.

When I asked Shimshon to describe a target memory from age 17, the time he was humiliated and dumped by the only girl he had ever dated, Shimshon kept mentioning The Cure, especially the songs "Love Song" and "Pictures of You." After our initial attempt to activate the memory failed, as evidenced by his report that "nothing is happening," we decided to add these songs in conjunction with BLS. Shimshon immediately reported having access to his emotions, which led to successful processing.

Another issue that often comes up for clients with histories of complex trauma is that they often remember an image as a fragment and not as a coherent picture. If they report a partial image—a shorter or blurred version of an image—work with what you have; it doesn't matter if the image is not clearly defined. Oftentimes, as your clients start processing, you (and often them as well) will be surprised by how much of the memory they retrieve. Some clients recover their memories like a jigsaw puzzle, adding piece after piece, and end up with a more coherent memory, which results in a more coherent narrative of their traumatic experience. As clients piece together this narrative, they usually experience a decrease in the disturbance associated with the traumatic memory.

In some situations, you can also work with imagined images, especially if clients were too young to remember the traumatic event or were traumatized vicariously (for example, in the case of a parent of a school shooting victim). For these clients, ask them to describe what they *imagine* happened. Work with the imagined image that represents the worst part of the memory. Once you and the client feel like you have the right image (or other sense), you can move on to the next core component: the negative cognition.

Target Component 2: The Negative Cognition

The negative cognition (NC) is not just a negative thought. It's an emotional thought that the client experiences in their head, as well as their heart and their gut. This repetitive thought tends to run on autopilot, whether the client is aware of it or not. Shapiro (2018) explains that the NC reflects the "client's current 'interpretation' of the self, not merely a description" (p. 54), meaning that the NC characterizes how the client relates to themselves and to the world. This cognition is more than just a thought; it's more like an operating system of thoughts that always runs in the background.

Oftentimes, your clients will verbalize the NC out loud for the first time when you ask them about it. For many clients, it can be a painful experience to say words like "I am weak" or "I'm a loser" out loud despite having this internal belief. But if it's hard for them to say these words, you probably have uncovered the right NC. Here are a few additional indicators that you have found the right NC:

- **It is an emotional thought, meaning that it is strongly linked to an emotion.** Shame and self-hatred are common among clients with histories of early childhood trauma. It is often evident in statements such as "I am not good enough" or "I don't belong."

- **It is a thought your client has about *themselves* (i.e., an "I" statement).** This can be hard for some clients to recognize, as they often tend to focus on other people, such as their abusers. It can be helpful to redirect clients to a self-referential statement by asking them, "What does it say about you?" when they provide a general negative thought.

- **It is a thought your client developed in the past but that they still feel in the present.** Clients tend to ignore adaptive information that is present and hold the NC as objective truth, despite evidence to the contrary.

- **It is verbalized in the present tense.** Since the NC feels present, it should be stated in the present tense. Aim for a thought that the client still believes about themselves today, and explain that while they cannot change what they thought about themselves in the past, successful EMDR processing will help change their present self-referential thoughts.

- **It is an irrational thought in that the NC doesn't reflect your client's present situation.** For example, a client with a loving spouse and caring friends might say, "I'm unlovable." Or a client who has fought hard to successfully overcome adversity might believe, "I am weak." Even though the NC is not true, these clients still *feel* unlovable or weak.

If a client cannot come up with the NC, it can be helpful to change the order of the protocol. Specifically, instead of probing for the NC right after inquiring about the image, you can ask about the image, emotions, and body sensations first—and only then about the cognition. Changing the order of the protocol can help you get an NC that originated in the right brain, as opposed to the left brain, which is important because negative cognitions are emotional thoughts. Remember that you're aiming to activate the memory network associated with moderate levels of arousal and that an emotional thought—one that originates in the right brain—is going to be more helpful in achieving this goal.

If reversing the order of the core target components doesn't help your client come up with an NC, consider starting to process the target memory without the cognition, and after a few sets, check in with them to see if they can think of any self-referential negative thought that goes with the memory.

For example, Yossef, a successful entrepreneur with low self-esteem, could not find an NC when we first began processing. After exploring a few NCs, and my unsuccessful attempt to reverse the order of the protocol, Yossef still couldn't come up with an NC. I decided to start processing the target memory without the NC and asked him to focus on the image, emotions, and body sensations that came to mind while applying BLS. After a few sets, I asked Yossef if there were any negative thoughts he had about himself that were associated with the memory. "I'm not good enough," he said without hesitation. By using the other three core components (image, emotion, and body sensations) to activate Yossef's memory network, the NC arose spontaneously.

Target Component 3: The Positive Cognition

The positive cognition (PC) is a thought the client chooses as an alternative to the NC, which allows them to think about themselves in a more adaptive way. For example, instead of thinking, "I am weak," the goal is for the client to believe, "I am strong." Or instead of thinking, "I have no control," to believe, "I am in control." When treatment is moving in the right direction, your client will develop an adaptive way of viewing themselves in which the PC replaces the NC. The shift happens when the client understands, on a deep level, the difference between "it happened to me" and "it happened." And when that shift occurs—when your client's "operating system" starts running on the PC (no pun intended)—it's a sign that they are moving in the right direction.

Here are some signs to help you determine if your clients have the right PC:

- **The PC is a thought that your client has about themselves and is verbalized in the present tense.** While the client might not yet believe the PC, this adaptive belief will be "installed" as they continue through phases 4 and 5.

- **The PC can be either positive or neutral.** Despite its name suggesting that it can only be a positive statement, the PC does not necessarily have to contradict the NC. More on that in a minute.

- **The PC is not a double negative.** For example, the PC could be "I'm smart" but not "I am not stupid." Since you are helping your client develop a new adaptive way of viewing themselves, you don't want them to only understand that the negative belief is not true; you want to "install" a brand new, adaptive belief.

- **The PC leads your client in the right direction and is on a continuum with the NC.** Believing in the PC helps the client understand that their previous, maladaptive beliefs (their NCs) were not true and did not represent reality.

- **The PC is a part of the desired outcome and not just as a part of the target memory.** When a client develops a new PC, it's not only about the target but about seeing their life through the lens of their new, adaptive PC. In other words, it should be what the client wants to believe about themselves in a broad, general sense.

In an ideal situation, the client's PC will negate their NC, but in many cases, they won't be able to think about a PC that directly contradicts the NC. In these situations, you can encourage them to choose a "process PC"—a neutral thought that moves them in the right direction but that does not necessarily negate the NC directly. It's enough for a process PC to be somewhere on a continuum between the NC and the PC. An example of a process PC would be "I am okay," or "I *can* be in control" (as opposed to "I am in control").

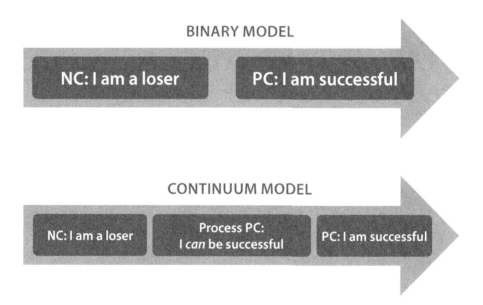

In addition, some clients will not have an answer when you ask them about their PC. This question can elicit feelings of frustration from both the client ("How can you ask me to think about anything positive when I am focused on my trauma?") and the therapist ("Why can't you just answer this question so we can move on with the protocol?"). If a client can't think of a PC, don't pressure them. It may make them feel as if you are not attuned to or lack empathy for their painful experience, especially if they have deep attachment wounds. In this case, you can wait until you're done with the desensitization phase to ask about the PC. Omitting the PC is also an option, especially when it compromises the therapeutic relationship (Parnell, 2006). If you start processing without the PC, you can skip over the next step—the validity of cognition (VOC) scale—during the assessment phase.

Target Component 4: The Validity of Cognition Scale

The validity of cognition (VOC) is a scale that rates how true the PC feels on a scale of 1 to 7. Many clients struggle with the VOC because it requires them to fit their subjective experience into a numeric scale. Since the VOC is not an objective measure, it can be influenced by factors outside of the therapy room, such as the amount of sleep the client got last night, the traffic they encountered on the way to your office, or a myriad of other circumstances.

For some clients, asking about the VOC can also be harmful because it triggers feelings of shame, frustration, and anger. This can happen when you ask them to rate their emotions on a scale, which can be perceived as insensitive and may have a negative impact on the therapeutic alliance. If your client cannot come up with a number, let it go. Don't compromise the most important predictor of treatment outcomes—the therapeutic relationship—just to get a number on a scale.

Remember that if you didn't get a PC from your client when setting up the target, you don't need to ask about the VOC. You can also omit the VOC if it is not appropriate to the client's circumstances.

For example, Naomi was a refugee from a village in rural Kenya. The oldest in a family of eight children, she never went to school and hadn't learned how to read or write. Naomi was illiterate not only in English (I saw her with an interpreter) but in her own language, Somali. When we processed her trauma, I decided to skip asking her about the VOC (even though she had a PC) because I knew she wouldn't understand the concept of rating her thought and placing it on a scale. Instead, I moved on to the next step and asked her about something she was able to relate to: her emotions.

Target Component 5: Emotion (or Emotions)

When asking clients about their emotions, remember that you want them to describe what they are feeling *now*. This is an important point, as the emotions your clients are feeling in the moment may be different from the emotions they experienced at the time of the trauma. While you cannot change what they felt in the past, you can change what they are feeling in the present with successful EMDR processing.

Your clients can feel one emotion or several emotions when thinking about their target memory. Don't limit the number of emotions. On the other hand, you don't need to ask them about additional emotions if they reported only one. Likewise, do not push them in the direction of emotions you think they should have. As with the NC and the PC, clients' emotions will change as you start processing. Instead, when you start processing, encourage them to "just notice" whatever emotions arise.

If clients find it hard to express their emotions in words, it can be helpful to explain to them that an emotion can generally be described in one word (e.g., sad, anxious, or angry). Some clients will still struggle and describe their emotions using *a lot* more than one word. For example, clients who experience anger toward their abusers may describe feeling like they are going to burst into flames or wanting to hurt their abusers. These clients often need to express their emotions with seemingly harsh words and with an affect that matches the intensity of their anger. As I discussed in chapter 3, it is important to give clients the time and the space to express themselves, as it provides them with a felt sense of safety and attunement in the therapeutic relationship that can help rewire maladaptive neural networks. If you try to rush clients through this process, it may harm your relationship with them and, in turn, compromise treatment outcomes.

Know, too, that emotions sometimes temporarily intensify during processing. It may seem like you're going in the wrong direction, but as long as the client's emotions continue to change, it means they are simply working through the processing phase. Emotions don't instantly become adaptive. For example, if a client has lived with the thought "I'm bad" for their whole life—and they now realize, for the first time, that their parents mistreated them throughout childhood—they may become angry before they move on to feeling acceptance and forgiveness. As you keep processing, the emotional change will move in the right direction and become more adaptive. This change can be either linear or nonlinear in nature.

Remember, EMDR therapy is not always as linear as you may have thought, especially when it comes to emotions. Emotions also don't have to become positive for adaptive resolution to occur. Oftentimes, clients' emotions transform from negative to neutral, which allows them to view themselves and the world more objectively. Either way, one of the indicators that a client has achieved adaptive resolution is when their emotions stop changing. When the client reports no change in emotions, this is a good time to check their SUD levels.

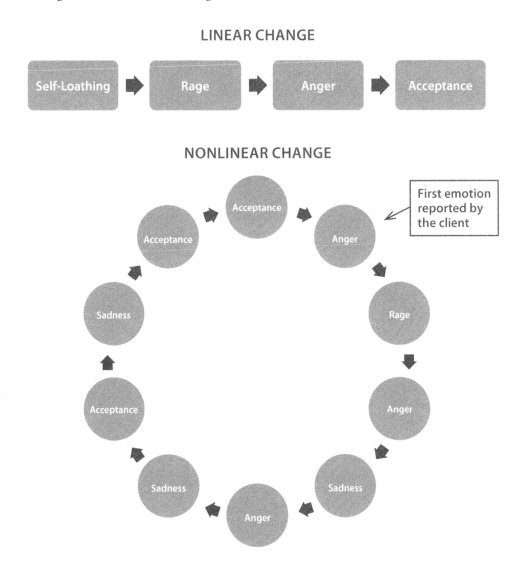

NONLINEAR CHANGE (ALTERNATIVE)

Target Component 6: The Subjective Unit of Disturbance Scale

The subjective unit of disturbance (SUD) scale is another marker to help you know if the processing is moving in the right direction. As its name suggests, this target component is subjective, so just like the VOC, it can be impacted by a variety of factors. That means if a client reported a SUD level of 5 last week, and today their SUD level is an 8, don't automatically assume it's because treatment is not going well. This increase in SUD level may reflect an argument they had with their boss right before the session started or some unsettling news they heard on the radio while driving over.

While you want to use the SUD scale right after clients identify the disturbing emotions associated with their target memory, Philip Manfield (2013) also recommends asking clients for their SUD levels during the history-taking phase or any time you consider a potential target memory for processing. That's because going through most of the assessment phase just to find out that a memory is not disturbing to your client may be a waste of your time. Asking about their SUD levels at earlier phases can help you identify the right targets from the get-go. Generally, processing targets with low levels of disturbance is not going to benefit your clients.

However, clients will sometimes report that a memory does not feel very disturbing as you set up the target, but after a few sets of BLS, they will experience a significant increase in disturbance. Although this can be very unpleasant for them (and for you), remember that SUD levels often increase before they decrease, which is a natural result of activating the memory networks associated with the trauma. As these networks become activated, your clients may experience more detailed images, thoughts, emotions, and body sensations that elicit distress. Therefore, before you start processing, make sure to explain to clients that they may experience a temporary increase in disturbance. Preparing them for this possibility can help reduce overwhelm during the desensitization phase.

Once a client's SUD levels finally do decrease, they won't always fall to 0—nor should you always expect them to. This notion probably runs counter to your basic EMDR training, where you learned that during phase 4, you need to desensitize until the client reports a SUD level of 0, and only then can you move on to installation. This is an ideal scenario that will happen in most cases, but there are exceptions to this rule. Take, for example, the case of a parent who lost a young child. It would be not only unrealistic but also insensitive to expect this client to experience a complete lack of disturbance when thinking about their child. In these kinds of situations, you can let go of the expectation of getting a SUD of 0 from your client.

Finally, know that in some situations, you can just omit the SUD rating altogether, particularly with clients who simply can't rate their emotion on a scale. (As one of my clients found it: "It will always be a 0 or a 10, nothing in the middle.") This is especially true when your clients are from a different culture. Our Western culture has an obsessive tendency to rate and measure everything, including emotions, but for others, this way of thinking is often not applicable. When you run into a situation in which asking about the client's SUD levels complicates things, use your clinical judgment and consider skipping it.

Target Component 7: Body Sensations

Clinical practice and a lot of research has led therapists to the conclusion that in order to do effective EMDR work, especially with trauma, we have to pay a lot of attention to the body. Remember that trauma leads to changes in the brain and nervous system that can follow people years after a traumatic event (van der Kolk, 2015). Many clients continue to produce large amounts of the stress hormone cortisol, which leads them to respond to present-day triggers as if the trauma were still happening. These triggers can be external (e.g., a loud sound or an angry face) or internal (e.g., an increase in heart rate or a strong sensation of pressure in the chest). In addition, physical sensations like an elevated heart rate are often over-coupled with emotions, so when you ask clients to focus on the physiological element of a memory, you are likely to access deep emotions. These body-emotions can lead to the retrieval of additional memories that have been repressed, often for many years.

Sometimes, the importance of body sensations requires you to go off script when processing with clients. For example, Zoheer was a refugee client from Sudan who I began seeing with the assistance of an interpreter. Whenever I asked him about the image, NC, or emotions associated with the target memory, he reported nothing. Instead, he tended to go back to the intense pressure he felt in his chest. I wasn't sure how to proceed and consulted with a sensorimotor psychotherapy consultant, who advised me to focus on desensitizing only his body sensations. After a few sets of focusing only on the intense pressure in his chest, Zoheer started crying. When I stopped the BLS to check in with him, he didn't have a lot to say. But as we kept going, the pressure in his chest changed, and over the next few months, he reported a significant reduction in his symptoms of depression.

Fast forward to two years later: Zoheer's English had improved enough that he was able to see me without an interpreter. At this point, our relationship had strengthened and he had learned to trust me. Without the presence of the interpreter, Zoheer disclosed that when he was nine years old, he had a few sexual encounters with his cousin. He explained that since then, he had felt intense guilt and shame. The processing we did two years earlier helped him reduce these emotions that were stuck in the body, improved his mood, and alleviated his physical symptoms. As Zoheer's story illustrates, when clients can't find the words to describe their internal experience, don't underestimate the power of working only with their body sensations.

However, some clients will not find it easy to access body sensations. In these situations, consider asking the client to close their eyes, as this can help them focus on any physical sensations that arise. But before you do that, you must always ask yourself whether the client is in their window of tolerance. If not, asking them to close their eyes can make things worse very quickly. It can cause flooding or dissociation (more on this in chapter 7). And the longer they close their eyes, the longer it will take you to help them regulate. Therefore, use your clinical judgment before asking clients to access body sensations this way.

A Holistic Approach to Targeting with Clusters

In basic EMDR training, you learned that in order to process trauma that has happened over a long period of time ("a cluster"), you have to identify the first, worst, and most recent memories during that time period. In theory, this is a good idea, as the rationale is that clients cannot process every single memory that happened over a period of time. By using this "first-worst-most recent" approach, it's thought that clients will experience a generalization effect that will help them process the whole time period.

But it's not that simple.

Here are some issues that often come up when processing clusters using this linear model:

- Oftentimes, clients cannot remember the first memory of the cluster.

- Many clients report having more than one worst memory in a cluster.

- Some clients are not regulated enough to process the worst target right away, but they are able to process a milder target. As is often the case with clients with complex trauma, starting with the first or worst memory may throw them out of their window of tolerance.

- Many clients have multiple targets and feel like they have to process more than just first-worst-most recent. Additionally, some clients don't remember the most recent memory in a cluster because these memories often consolidate together, and it's hard to separate the "most recent" memory from other, similar memories.

- Sometimes what the client believed was the first memory turns out not to be the first target. As the client starts processing, earlier memories resurface. Once the floodgates are open, memories that had been repressed for many years come spilling out, and the client quickly realizes that what they thought was their earliest memory was not, in fact, the first.

- Likewise, sometimes what the client thought was their worst memory is superseded by an even more disturbing memory. This can happen when the client has several similar memories that happened around the same time as the "worst" memory, or when implicit memories become more explicit throughout processing. Even when a client is confident that they know what target they need to process, there is always the possibility that a more difficult memory will be uncovered during the course of processing.

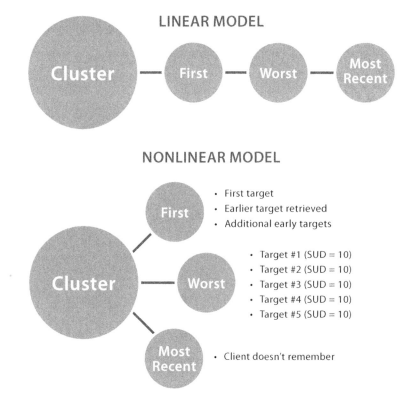

The case of Oded illustrates a nonlinear approach to working with clusters. The first 18 years of Oded's life were, quite literally, one big cluster. As a nonbinary queer person and the child of ultra-conservative parents, Oded had to hide their true identity until they left their parents' house and went to college. During this time, Oded had to pretend that they were someone else in every situation: at home, at school, and especially at church.

After a lot of preparation work, we started processing their attachment wounds and processed many, many incidents for several months. The more Oded learned about the healing power of EMDR and how it helped transform their memories and change their emotions, the more memories they wanted to process. When we were done with our processing work, Oded was able to fully accept themselves—something they were never able to do before. This wouldn't have been possible if we had only targeted the first, worst, and most recent memories.

The EMDR Model Is Linear—Real EMDR Is Not

Because EMDR is taught as a phase-based model, in which each phase is independent, many therapists conclude that EMDR processing is inflexible. They believe that once they are done with phase 1, they have to move to phase 2, and only then to phase 3, so on and so forth. But therapy (EMDR included) doesn't work like that. As you've learned, EMDR is not a linear process, and real EMDR work cannot be rigid. If you conceptualize your clients' journeys as a linear process, it will make you less intuitive and less attuned to your clients' ever-changing needs, causing disappointment for you and for your clients. While you want to have an end goal—adaptive resolution—your clients' journeys toward this goal are always unique.

Therefore, in addition to the tools mentioned in this chapter, here are a few ways to adopt a more holistic approach and remain open to the process unfolding:

- **Start with phase 2.** Some clients will enter therapy in a state of dysregulation and be unable to start talking about their past. In this case, you may need to start with phase 2 (preparation) before you can start phase 1 (history taking).

- **Take a break.** If you start desensitizing a target memory in phase 4 and your client becomes too overwhelmed to process the target (i.e., their SUD levels don't change and they appear out of their window of tolerance), you may have to take a break. In this case, revisit phase 2 and help them regulate their nervous system by introducing more emotion regulation tools.

- **Combine more than one phase.** When working with clients who have experienced complex trauma, you may have to titrate the processing for a few seconds, use calming techniques, and go back and forth between desensitization (phase 4) and resourcing (phase 2). This represents the process of dual awareness I discussed in chapter 4.

- **Split phases 3 and 4.** When you practiced in basic EMDR training, things usually went smoothly between the assessment and the desensitization phases. You likely transitioned fluently according to the linear model. But in a real EMDR session, things don't necessarily move on a line. Oftentimes, you will start the assessment phase but not have enough time to start desensitization until the next session. When that happens, make sure you leave time to close the session, especially for clients who struggle to regulate their emotions. The assessment phase can be activating to some clients, so be sure to help them recognize and regulate their feelings and reduce any disturbances as needed.

These are just a few examples that illustrate why EMDR is not and cannot be linear. This change in perspective will help your case conceptualization and your EMDR work in general. It will prevent you from feeling disappointed when your clients don't move on a line. Now, let's move on to discussing how to start actively processing, which is the focus of the next chapter.

CHAPTER 7

Where the Magic of EMDR Happens

· ·

From the client's perspective, the goal of treatment is often solely the relief from debilitating symptoms. For the practicing clinician who is well-versed in EMDR, however, the ultimate aim is to enhance the client's ability to love both self and others and to engender a new joy in living, in addition to banishing overt suffering.

—Francine Shapiro, foreword in Manfield, *Extending EMDR*

· ·

In this chapter, I will get into the core of EMDR phases 4 through 6, in which clients are actively processing target memories. During these phases, you will see the magic of EMDR happening, often right before your eyes. These processing phases lead to the most dramatic shifts in clients' brains and, as a result, in their psyches. When processing is complete, your client's symptoms will cease and their memories will change from emotional to neutral as they get to a state of adaptive resolution. This is the most transformative part of the EMDR journey, and it is incredibly exciting when it goes well.

But processing is also what many EMDR therapists and clients are scared of. During the processing phases, things can *feel* wrong, and it is during these phases that things can sometimes *go* wrong. During these phases, some clients will loop, abreact, and dissociate. This can lead both clients and therapists to become overwhelmed.

What Are Abreactions?

Abreaction is a discharge of affect that occurs when unconscious material—memories that have been repressed—comes back to consciousness (Hensley, 2016). Some clients experience abreactions somatically, with strong physical sensations, while others abreact with intense emotions. When clients process traumatic experiences, you are instructing them to notice the same emotional or somatic experience they had during the worst part of their trauma. In doing so, you should prepare them for the possibility that they will experience intense emotions and physical sensations. If your clients (and you) are caught off guard and not ready for the possibility of this intense emotional discharge, abreaction can be a very scary experience. But if you are prepared, and you understand abreaction as a natural experience on the path to healing, you can reduce the overwhelm that some clients and therapists experience when clients abreact.

Therefore, the goal of this chapter is to reduce your overwhelm and help you navigate phases 4 through 6 with confidence, competence, and flow. I'll also touch on how to return clients to a sense of safety in phase 7 and examine their progress in phase 8. Much of what I'll discuss in this chapter is what you *didn't* learn in your basic EMDR training. I'll provide you with step-by-step guidance to supplement what you already know from basic training to help you practice EMDR with more flexibility. In particular, you'll learn how to:

- Use the window of tolerance to determine your clients' readiness for processing

- Improve phase 4 (desensitization)

- Upgrade phase 5 (installation)

- Go deeper with phase 6 (body scan)

- Leave time for phase 7 (closure)

- Check in during phase 8 (reevaluation)

My hope is that reading this chapter will help you continue thinking about EMDR as a nonbinary model and understand that most of what you do in therapy is not black or white. This understanding will help you be more creative in your work and practice EMDR with flow.

Now that you know what to expect from this chapter, here's a short note on what you won't learn: specialty protocols. Over the past few years, a growing number of these protocols have been created by EMDR trainers, consultants, and practitioners. In theory, more protocols to choose from can seem beneficial, but in reality, they can cause unnecessary overwhelm when therapists become fixated on trying to find the "right" protocol for clients' problems, conditions, or diagnoses. While some of these protocols can be effective, you will not become a better EMDR therapist by superficially knowing a large number of specialty protocols. Instead, what I have found is that, in most cases, the standard protocol can be adapted to fit each client's needs and resolve whatever issue brought them to my office (Marich & Dansiger, 2021).

This means that your first step toward EMDR proficiency starts with being fluent in the standard protocol. You have to know the basics first. You will learn how to master it, and after you master it, you will learn how to be creative with it. But first, let's discuss how the window of tolerance relates to your clients' readiness to start processing.

The Window of Tolerance

During EMDR processing, you intentionally activate the neural networks that hold your client's disturbing memories. Although intense emotions are not a prerequisite for successful EMDR treatment, they are very common during the processing phases, mostly during desensitization. Therefore, before you activate these emotional memories, you want to make sure the client is ready for processing. In addition to the common questions that can help you determine whether your client is ready to proceed (mentioned in chapter 4), one of the most important indicators to let you know your client is ready for processing is whether or not they are in the window of tolerance.

The *window of tolerance* is a term coined by Dan Siegel (1999) that allows you to determine what is happening in your client's nervous systems in real time. It helps you detect issues like stuck processing, dissociation, and overstimulation so you know when and how to intervene. When a client is *in* the window of tolerance, their sympathetic and parasympathetic nervous systems work in a state of coherence and they feel regulated (Childre & Rozman, 2005). They are balanced. Effective EMDR processing can only happen when your client is in this window—in "the processing zone." In this state, your client is able to maintain dual awareness and look at their disturbing memories with objectivity. They can become the observer, which, as I mentioned in chapter 5, is necessary for successful processing.

But when a client is *outside* the window of tolerance, things can get messy very quickly. They can go into a state of hyperarousal or hypoarousal, depending on which branch of their autonomic nervous system becomes activated. If the sympathetic nervous system goes into overdrive, the client will go in a state of hyperarousal where they become anxious, angry, and overstimulated. When that happens, your client may experience physical symptoms, like increased heart rate and shallow breathing. Their speech may be fast, and they may appear agitated or restless.

On the other hand, if a client's parasympathetic nervous system becomes hyperactive, they can go in a state of hypoarousal in which they disengage, numb out, or dissociate. When that happens, your client will get lost in the memories of the past and will be unable to maintain dual awareness. Dissociation can be like a time machine that transports your client to their painful past. Effective EMDR processing cannot happen when the client is highly dissociated.

Finally, if both the sympathetic and parasympathetic branches of the nervous system become overactivated at the same time, "a fairly intolerable, disorganizing sensation is created, akin to jamming accelerator and brakes to the floor at the same time" (Badenoch, 2008, p. 21). In this state, your client can go back and forth between feeling flooded and disengaged—a situation that can be confusing for clinician and client alike.

Remember that processing will likely bring emotions—this is sometimes unavoidable. But in either case of overactivation, the client's emotions may make it difficult, and in some cases, impossible, to effectively process. Therefore, monitoring your client's window of tolerance and helping them stay in the processing zone is a prerequisite to a successful EMDR treatment.

In your basic EMDR training, you learned the window of tolerance looks like this:

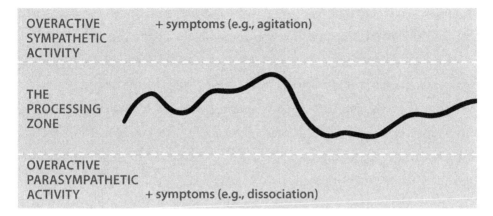

But it can also look like this:

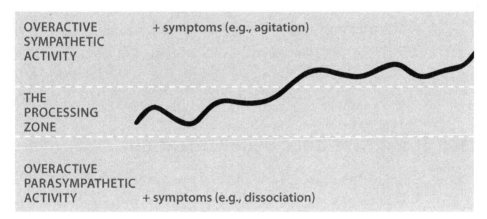

Or like this:

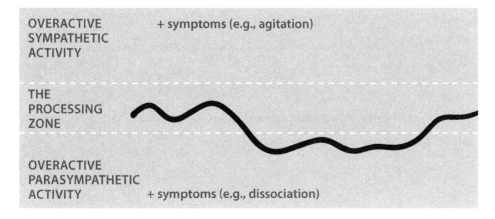

Just as each person has a unique way that they process information, they also have a different nervous system, so their individual window of tolerance is not the same as anyone else's. Regulated clients have a wider window of tolerance (meaning it takes something significant to push them outside their window), while anxious clients and those with dissociative tendencies have a narrower window of tolerance (meaning they can get pushed outside their window by even minor triggers). The wider a client's window of tolerance, the easier it is for them to regulate emotions and effectively process disturbing memories.

Your goal as you prepare your clients for processing is to ensure that their window of tolerance is wide enough to handle the emotional intensity that EMDR can bring. Widening the window of tolerance is an ongoing process that happens over time with consistent practice. As discussed in chapter 5, this process can be achieved through a regular meditation practice. It can also be done with the use of effective coping skills, like breathing techniques, the Safe and Sound Protocol (SSP), or any other method that can help clients regulate their nervous systems. Activities such as acupuncture, massage, chi gong, or even regular physical exercise can be very effective and should be individualized to your clients' personal preferences.

Phase 4: Improve Your Desensitization

Once you determine that a client is ready to begin processing, it's time to move on to phase 4: desensitization. Some of the most noticeable differences will happen during this phase as your client desensitizes their memories. Here, you will witness how your client's memories transform from psychological memories to objective memories (Parnell, 1997). This transformation is an individual experience that could never be limited to a script or a protocol because all clients have different ways of processing information. Some tend to be triggered by thoughts, others by emotions, and still others by body sensations. Therefore, during this phase, the four core components of a target (image, cognitions, emotions, and sensations) will not be divided equally into four equal quarters.

Your clients' targets will rarely look like this:

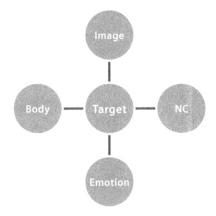

And will more often look like this:

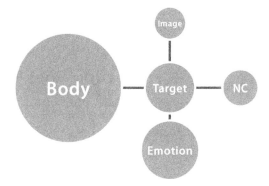

Or this:

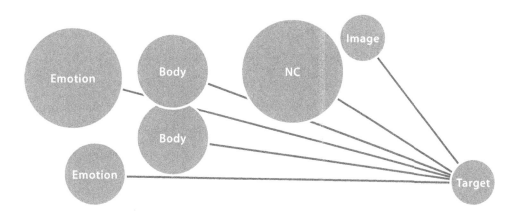

Or this:

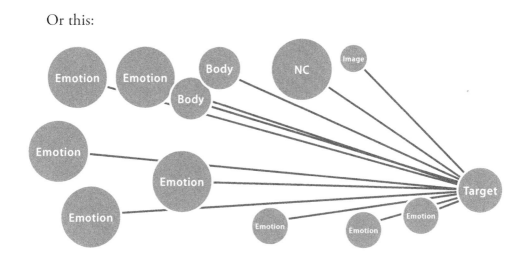

Every EMDR session looks and feels different. Personalizing your approach and staying attuned to what your clients need in each and every moment is the most important thing to remember when clients are in the desensitization phase.

Stay Out of the Way (When Processing Goes Well)

When beginning processing, Shapiro (2018) famously suggested that "both clinician and client must try to stay out of the way as much as possible" (p. 122). You should use this advice when processing is flowing smoothly, but when you run into issues (which happens more often than not), you have to intervene. For example, if a client is unable to maintain dual awareness and quickly dissociates, staying out of their way will not only lead to ineffective EMDR processing, but it may harm them and potentially lead to a deterioration of their mental state.

Let me say that again: **If processing doesn't work flawlessly, you have to intervene.** But before you intervene with a script, protocol, or other technique, you must try to understand *why* the processing is stuck to begin with. Instead of trying to follow the latest and greatest technique, stop for a second and try to understand what is happening to your client. What's going on inside their brain, body, and nervous system? What is preventing them from being able to process the target memory? Understanding the reasons why processing has gotten stuck will help you find the right intervention by using your logic, as opposed to relying on more scripts, procedures, and protocols. Only after uncovering the "why" can you determine a solution.

Why Processing Gets Stuck

Conceptually, you can understand stuck processing as the lack of synthesis of neural networks. When processing is stuck, the adaptive networks don't fire at the same time as the maladaptive networks, and when these networks don't fire in sync, they don't integrate with each other. When processing is stuck, clients will report no changes in the four core components of the target. The image, NC, emotions, and body sensations will often stay the same after several sets of BLS, and the SUD levels won't change either. Clients are also likely to report that "nothing is happening."

WHEN PROCESSING IS STUCK
(No Integration of Networks)

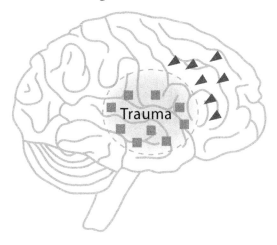

WHEN PROCESSING GOES WELL
(Integration of Adaptive and Maladaptive Networks)

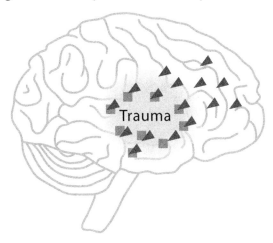

While issues may come up in any phase of EMDR, getting stuck is most common during the desensitization phase. Here are some of the most common reasons this can occur:

- **The therapeutic relationship is not yet strong enough.** Starting the desensitization phase before establishing a strong therapeutic relationship, especially with clients with complex childhood trauma and attachment wounds, often results in stuck processing.

- **Your client is out of the window of tolerance.** As I've mentioned, when a client is out of their window, processing cannot be done effectively. Therefore, make sure you stay attuned to your client's level of arousal when processing, and use emotion regulation strategies or grounding techniques if your client is sliding out of their window. Remember, too, that your nervous system syncs with your clients' nervous systems, so when you help your clients process trauma, you will witness (and sometimes feel) a lot of emotional intensity. You will see your clients experience some of their most painful emotions, like shame, rage, fear, anxiety, and panic. If you don't ground yourself in these moments, you may find yourself outside of your window of tolerance when clients become dysregulated. Therefore, just as you must remain attuned to your clients' window of tolerance, keep track of your own window as well.

- **There is an earlier target.** Oftentimes, when processing a target, there is an earlier memory that you and your client don't know about. Stuck processing often happens when the earlier target memory is related to the memory you are processing. Processing may not progress until you find and process the earlier target.

- **Ego states (or parts) interfere with processing.** Different parts modalities, such as ego state therapy, internal family systems (IFS), and the developmental needs meeting strategy (DNMS), have different terminologies for parts, but they all agree on one thing: EMDR processing gets stuck because ego states interfere with the processing.

- **Your client has no access to the memory.** This can happen when clients are "too much in the present" or when a memory has been repressed and stored as an implicit memory. Processing memories that clients cannot access explicitly is more challenging than processing targets of explicit memories.

- **Your client has "both feet in the past."** When clients are unable to maintain dual awareness and can't feel the safety of the present, processing becomes stagnant. When that happens, clients oftentimes disengage and sometimes dissociate.

- **Your client has certain limiting beliefs.** When clients have limiting beliefs about themselves (e.g., "I will never get better"), it often limits their ability to effectively process target memories.

- **You're working on the wrong target.** Sometimes processing doesn't progress simply because you're not processing the right target. As I mentioned earlier, clients sometimes believe they know what memory needs to be processed but later find out that they were not "on target." Other memories often emerge during the desensitization phase, including (1) chronologically earlier memories or (2) memories that are thematically related to the original memory. If you or your client realizes that you are processing the wrong target memory, make sure you set up a new target memory and start processing it.

- **Your client is prone to flooding.** Some clients have difficulties with focusing on a target and experience rapid thoughts and emotions, which can result in flooding. This is particularly the case for clients with histories of complex trauma, as they often struggle with emotion regulation. These clients cannot handle processing images, thoughts, emotions, and body sensations for extended periods of time, and when that happens, their nervous systems will lose balance and they will get thrown out of their window of tolerance very quickly. When working with these clients, make sure to consult with an EMDR consultant who specializes in this population so you can learn specific strategies that were not covered in basic EMDR training.

- **There are secondary gains and losses involved.** Is your client going to lose anything as a result of successful processing? Is adaptive resolution going to lead to a change in their identity? These types of secondary gains and losses can have a negative effect on processing.

- **Your client didn't sleep well.** Sometimes limited results happen during phase 4 due to insomnia or lack of adequate sleep. Clients who don't get regular sleep often report lack of progress in processing. During dream sleep, certain neurochemical changes occur in the brain that "essentially act to switch the software running the brain" (Zadra & Stickgold, 2021, p. 118). When your clients' brains don't get a "software update," they are less likely to be ready for processing.

12 Interventions That Will Help You When Processing Is Stuck

Now that I've explained some reasons why processing can get stuck, here are some interventions that will help you get *unstuck*. In order to get better results, remember to always understand the reasons why processing got stuck in the first place so you can personalize these interventions for each client's needs.

- **Stop processing.** Sometimes stopping the processing is the best thing for the client, and it will give you time to think about which intervention to use. When you recognize that your client is out of their window of tolerance or when they feel like they need to regulate, don't hesitate to take a break. Remember that it's not a race and that good treatment needs good conceptualization. Sometimes you'll need to reassess the targets you're working on with your client or consider using different strategies. Taking a break from processing will allow you to do that.

- **Change the BLS.** You can change the speed, the form (e.g., tactile to eye movements), and the direction (e.g., tilt your lightbar from horizontal to diagonal) of the BLS. You can also increase the intensity of your tappers, change the length of the BLS sets, or add another form of BLS (e.g., add tactile BLS to eye movements).

- **Help your client stay in the window of tolerance.** There are many tools you can use to accomplish this. Regulating the breath with square breathing (four-second inhale, four-second hold, four-second exhale, and four-second hold) is just one of many breathing techniques that can help clients stay in their window. A grounding smell, like lavender essential oil, can also be soothing for some clients and help them get back in their window. These strategies can be done between sets or can be integrated into BLS sets. For example, if a client tends to become dysregulated during the desensitization phase, you can instruct them to notice a soothing smell while focusing on the target memory.

- **Explore the possibility of earlier targets.** Find out about earlier target memories by asking your client if there are any earlier memories that come up, or by using the floatback technique. The floatback is a technique that uses some or all of the four core components of a target to activate a memory network that is linked to an earlier memory. Ask your client to focus on the image, NC, emotions, and body sensations (or only one or some of these elements) and instruct them to "let your mind float back to an earlier time in your life when you may have felt this way before, and just notice what comes to mind" (Shapiro, 2018, p. 200).

- **Explore your client's internal system.** Learning how to effectively work with parts requires more advanced trainings and consultations; however, you can explain to clients that we all have complex internal systems made up of parts (or ego states) who all have different agendas. Clients with severe trauma often have parts with intense negative emotions toward each other. For this reason, it's important to establish trust with these parts, as they may interfere with the processing phase of EMDR. A very basic exercise you can do without any formal training is to improve communication between the client's current adult self and their child parts. You can do this by asking, "What would your adult self say to the child?" or "What does the child need?" When the clients responds with an answer, help them to just "notice that" with BLS.

- **Ask your client to shift their attention to body sensations.** If the client has limited access to the memory, try directing them to somatic memories by noticing their body sensations. Ask, "What do you notice in your body?" and direct them to "notice that." Remember that there are generally two types of memory: explicit (conscious) and implicit (unconscious). Processing often becomes stagnant when clients focus on explicit aspects of their memories and don't pay attention to implicit memories. Focusing on clients' body sensations can help them access the unconscious memories that are implicitly stored in their brains and bodies.

- **Add a supportive figure or a resource team.** Sometimes, it is easier to accomplish things with a little help. Try adding a supportive figure, like a wise, nurturing, or protective ally (Parnell, 2007), to your clients' resources, or mobilize an entire resource team (Schmidt, 2020). These resources are designed to support your clients when accessing disturbing memories.

  For example, I once worked with a client named Oren, who was the oldest of three children. His father was detached and his mother was mostly anxious. When we began phase 4, we decided to start processing a memory in which a group of children assaulted him with metal rods, kicked his face, and humiliated him for what felt like forever. But we became stuck: Oren's SUD levels did not drop, and we both felt anger toward the kids who abused him. After trying different interventions that didn't work, we decided to use a protective ally. Oren chose Sylvester Stallone, in the form of Rambo, who joined him in the target memory. Oren reported that with the help of Rambo, he was able to "give those kids what they deserved." His SUD level immediately dropped from 10 to 5 and continued dropping as we went on with processing. With clients who have histories of complex trauma and attachment wounds, you want to start adding supports during the preparation phase.

- **Instruct your client to keep their eyes open or closed.** Depending on why your client's processing is stuck, opening or closing their eyes can help. If the client is unable to process because the memory is too disturbing and feels like it is occurring in the present, instruct them to keep their eyes open when processing. In contrast, if they are unable to process because they can't access the memory, consider asking them to keep their eyes closed and use tapping or tactile BLS.

- **Help your client create distance from disturbing images.** If a client is experiencing difficulties with disturbing memories, you can help them create some distance from the disturbance by imagining a glass screen between them and the image, shrinking their perpetrator, or turning the whole image into black and white.

- **Use interweaves.** Interweaves are interventions that help introduce a new, adaptive perspective when processing gets stuck. This involves offering clients new information in the form of a question or statement that mimics spontaneous processing (Hensley, 2016). When a client develops a maladaptive belief, consider asking them questions that will challenge this perspective. For example, if they say, "It was my fault" when describing a continuous sexual abuse by their stepfather, you can ask, "If it was your niece who was sexually abused, would you say it was her fault?" The answer seems obvious, but it requires using an adaptive, adult perspective, which should help "jump-start" the spontaneous processing. The more you know about your clients and their belief systems, the better interweaves you will have access to. When using interweaves, think not only about the different categories (e.g., responsibility, safety, choice), but consider your clients' internal systems and help their child parts understand what the adult already knows.

- **Use EMD.** EMD can help when clients become flooded by intense thoughts, emotions, body sensations, and related memories. EMD is a technique that focuses on desensitizing (but not reprocessing—hence the missing *R*) memories. When you use EMD, you limit associative memories that are not directly related to the specific target you started processing. When the client reports having associations that are not directly related to the original memory, you gently redirect them back to the target and ask them to rate their SUD level associated with that memory. By asking them to rate their

SUD level (instead of asking, "What did you notice?"), you keep them on target and prevent them from experiencing free associations that would lead them to other (potentially overwhelming) memories.

- **Brainstorm with your client.** If none of these strategies help, ask your client why they think processing is stuck. Are they aware of a possible secondary gain (or loss)? Are they too afraid to access the memory? Your clients will often have the answers.

What to Do When Clients Dissociate

Although many therapists are afraid of working with clients who dissociate, the reality is that dissociation is a normal human function (Marich & Dansiger, 2021). In fact, most of us dissociate at some point in our lives without being assigned a clinical diagnosis, and many gifted individuals in different professions, including spiritual leaders, therapists, and even EMDR trainers, have dissociative minds (Marich, 2023). Therefore, instead of fearing dissociation, I encourage you to embrace the dissociated mind. Normalizing the experience of dissociation is important because many of your clients will dissociate during phase 4, and if you become overwhelmed when this happens, you are less likely to be effective in helping your clients.

When clients dissociate during processing, first take a breath and remind yourself that they are okay and that you now have a very clear short-term goal: to orient them to the present moment. When clients dissociate, they can lose orientation to the present, as they tend to travel back in time. One way to understand dissociation is by understanding your clients' internal systems through the lens of parts work. As mentioned previously, parts work therapies believe each client has multiple parts, and each part has different ways of thinking, different emotional states, and different models of reality. Some parts, mostly younger and hurt ones, tend to dissociate in response to intense emotions (or sometimes in response to any emotions).

Taking advanced trainings and consultations in parts work can help take your EMDR therapy to the next level, but there are several strategies you can use right now for clients who are dissociating. Here are five quick ways you can orient your client back to the present moment—to what's in front of them:

- **Ask your client to take their shoes off.** Guide your client to feel the ground and notice the subtle sensations in their feet.

- **Use an essential oil diffuser.** Keep a diffuser in a central location in your office, and turn it on with a grounding smell, such as lavender.

- **Play pass with your client.** Use a stress ball or other small object and pass it back and forth between the two of you.

- **Have your client use their senses.** Ask your client to identify three things that they see, two that they hear, and one that they sense in the room.

- **Have your client count.** They can count sheep, go from 1 to 100, or subtract sevens from a number like 1,569. The act of counting helps to tax the client's working memory resources (Matthijssen et al., 2021), which can reduce the intensity and vividness of emotional memories and help bring their attention to the present moment.

Once you are able to reground your client in the here and now, proceed with caution. They may or may not be ready to immediately resume processing work. They sometimes need a break, and the best way to find out what they need is to simply ask them. Some clients get overwhelmed by the dissociative experience and the loss of orientation to the present moment. With these clients, you want to make sure not to pressure them to restart processing and instead provide them with more skills that will help them remain grounded and regulated. When you resume processing, you want to start slow and test the client's responses to processing. You can do that by applying BLS for very short periods of time (short sets) and using only one of the core components of a target memory, instead of all four (image, NC, emotions, and body sensations) at the same time.

Flow Between Phases

Therapeutic modalities like EMDR are conceptualized, developed, and taught as phase-based models so they can become accepted by the scientific community. Because scientists tend to think in a linear way—in phases—therapeutic modalities are developed as phased-based. It's for this reason that in basic EMDR training, therapists learn that only after they're done with phase 4, and the client reports a SUD level of 0, can they move on to phase 5: the installation phase. But as I've discussed, natural healing processes like EMDR cannot and should not be limited to this way of thinking.

More likely than not during EMDR therapy, the natural flow of phases will start weaving into each other, and you will sometimes find that the installation phase naturally integrates into the desensitization phase. When this happens, embrace it. For example, if a client starts to notice their NC has changed to a PC, let them go with that. This change is a reflection of adaptive material being integrated into their maladaptive neural network. You don't want to stop this natural healing process because you're in phase 4 and "installation only happens in phase 5." Remember that your job is to strengthen these adaptive networks. After a number of sets, ask the client to go back to the original target. More often than not, they will report a significant reduction in their SUD levels. Natural integration has begun!

Eventually, when the client tells you that they have no disturbance, then you can fluently transition to phase 5: installation.

Phase 5: Upgrade the Installation

During the installation phase, your goal is to install and strengthen a new, adaptive PC that is associated with the target. As I discussed in chapter 6, the PC can lie on a continuum between a positive thought and neutral thought (often referred to as a "process PC"). Sometimes clients can only come up with a neutral thought because they continue to hold some limiting schemas (e.g., "I don't matter"), and this neutral thought is the best representation of how they view themselves. As a therapist, you will be able to see positive qualities in clients that they cannot see in themselves. In this case, you can explore with them the possibility of "upgrading" their PCs.

For example, let's say that your client reports the PC "I'm okay," but you know that they are more than okay—they are good, or even great. This is exactly how I felt working with Maya, a client in her late thirties who had generations of trauma in her family. Maya was successful in every aspect of her life—she had a loving husband, a successful and fulfilling career, two young and healthy children, and many friends—but she was still unable to come up with a PC about herself. "I'm okay" was all she could think of when I asked her about a PC.

In response, I shared with Maya that I recognized her as being so much more than "okay." I helped Maya see herself through my eyes, which made her open to seeing herself in a different light. As a result, she developed the upgraded PC "I am successful," which helped negate not only her NC but also her old schemas. I have used this approach with numerous clients who tend to narrow their PC to their old limiting beliefs. With a little exploration and encouragement, clients start seeing themselves as more than "okay."

The installation of this new belief system is an essential part of your clients' healing journeys, but it is not the only part. You also want to include other components of the associative memory network during the installation phase, and this can't happen if you only focus on cognitions. It's important to remember that the PC makes up just one part of a larger neural network comprising many other elements, such as sounds, smells, emotions, and body sensations (Lipke, 1999). If you limit the installation to cognitions only and fail to include these other elements of the adaptive neural network, you will miss out on an opportunity to give your clients a deeper positive experience of the installation.

For instance, if you're installing the PC "I'm lovable," but you don't extend the installation beyond the level of cognition, the client will miss out on the deeper aspects of their new belief system, such as the feeling of being lovable or the somatic sensations that they experience when feeling loved. Therefore, when adopting a holistic approach to the installation phase, think about strengthening the *entire* adaptive network as a whole.

Remember to pay particular attention to adaptive physical sensations, like body posture, a relaxed feeling in the face, and sensations near the heart. Installing positive physical sensations in general—and improving posture in particular—will allow for a major upgrade to the installation experience. With this upgrade, clients learn to increase body awareness and widen their window of tolerance. If a client notices a feeling of strength in their lower back during the installation, use it as an opportunity to strengthen it with BLS. Help them notice what they are feeling in their body, and explore how it makes them feel about themselves and how the new somatic sensations can be integrated into their life outside of the therapy session.

INSTALLING ONLY THE COGNITION

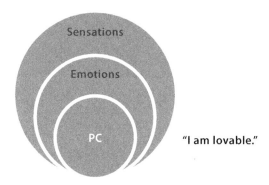

INSTALLING THE NEW NEUTRAL NETWORK

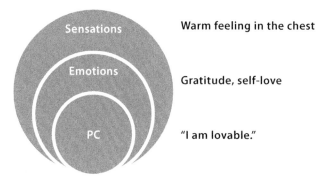

Slow It Down

In addition to focusing on the entire adaptive network during the installation phase, make sure to *slow it down*. In basic EMDR training, many therapists learn to speed through the installation phase and, as a result, miss out on important opportunities to enhance their clients' new, adaptive belief systems. If a client reports a VOC of 7, but they keep experiencing new adaptive material, why stop there? You have to remember that Shapiro created the VOC scale with a very specific goal in mind: to validate EMDR and help categorize it as an evidence-based modality. While we should all be thankful that Shapiro included the use of scales to validate EMDR, that doesn't mean that healing stops at 7. This is simply an arbitrary number that signifies the upper end of the VOC scale. If the client reports that adaptive material is continuing to show up, keep going at a steady pace—don't speed through the process.

Installation or Instillation?

As a therapist, your job is to instill hope in your clients. Not only is hope necessary to keep clients in therapy, but "faith in a treatment mode can in itself be therapeutically effective" (Yalom, 1995, p. 4). Therefore, during the installation phase, you are not only installing a new PC or an adaptive network—you are instilling hope. You are demonstrating to your client not only that change is possible in the future but that positive change has already started. As I will soon discuss, a lot of this change happens below the level of consciousness—at the level of the nervous system—where verbal language doesn't exist.

Phase 6: Body Scan Done Better

During phase 6 of EMDR, your goal is to help the client discharge any remaining tension from their body. You do so by guiding them to scan their body after installing the PC and instructing them to notice the subtlest physical sensations that arise. This can help them recognize any feelings that are somatically trapped in the body, which you can then target for processing. The body scan can be especially helpful for clients who are "stuck in their heads" and are not particularly good at expressing their emotions in words.

Traditional EMDR suggests that you start the body scan by asking the client to close their eyes and bring to mind the original target memory and PC (Shapiro, 2018). However, since the original memory has changed during the desensitization and installation phases, I believe that a better instruction is to instead ask the client to bring up the *current* version of the memory, or the memory as it appears to them now, and to then notice any sensations in their body.

Learning the Body's Language

Although the body scan is an important phase of EMDR, it is another portion that therapists often speed through without paying attention to details. This is a result of what many therapists are taught in basic EMDR training, where they learn to instruct the client to scan their body from head to toe and quickly move on. However, when you rush through the body scan, you are missing a lot of deep emotions that cannot be expressed in words—emotions that need to be processed.

Remember that the thinking brain, the feeling brain, and the sensing brain each have a different way of processing information, so emotions can't always be translated into words. Instead, they often make themselves evident as bodily sensations. For example, grief might present itself as a feeling of emptiness in the stomach, while terror can be expressed somatically as tightness in the chest. By doing a body scan, clients can learn to listen to the language of the nervous system—a language that can inform them about disturbances they didn't notice in previous phases because words failed to express the disturbance. But the body remembers.

To teach your clients the language of the nervous system, ask them to bring to mind the target memory and PC while they scan their bodies and notice any physical sensations that arise. If they want to know why you are asking them to scan their body, explain that most of our emotional processes originate from the bottom up (i.e., from the body to the brain) as opposed to the top down (i.e., from the brain to the body). With bottom-up processing, they move from sensations to emotions to thoughts—noticing what information their sensations provide as they flow from the body to the brain. As these sensations can provide useful information, you want to help clients resist the temptation to quickly switch to a top-down approach. When clients operate from the top down, they tend to rationalize, interpret, and find explanations after every BLS set. This is very different from just noticing, something that is very hard for many clients, especially those with histories of complex childhood trauma.

TOP-DOWN PROCESSING VERSUS BOTTOM-UP PROCESSING

Top Down	Bottom Up

Prefrontal Cortex	THINKING		Prefrontal Cortex	THINKING
Limbic System	FEELING		Limbic System	FEELING
Body	SENSING		Body	SENSING

Bottom-up processing can be difficult for clients with histories of physical and sexual abuse who have learned to ignore the sensations in their bodies. Other severely traumatized clients experience intense body sensations when they feel anxious, depressed, or triggered by reminders of the trauma. You can help these clients with bottom-up processing by teaching them to recognize and stay with any physical discomfort as it arises. As clients learn to observe these sensations, they develop the ability to sit with them for just a few seconds longer. If at any time they start bringing up old thinking patterns, gently suggest that they notice the "raw data"—the bodily sensations. When clients learn to approach their physical discomfort with more curiosity and spend a little more time in each set while applying BLS, you teach them another way to widen their window of tolerance.

Using the body scan to its full potential can make a big difference on the path to adaptive resolution, so whenever clients say that they don't notice anything in their bodies, encourage them to take their time. Help them notice even the most subtle sensations. Educate them on the language of the body, and explain that if they will just listen, they will become familiar with this language. And don't forget to remind them that learning the language of the body, like learning any new language, takes time and practice.

Use the Body Scan to Enhance Positive Sensations

Now that you know how to use the body scan to detect nonverbal disturbances, let's talk about another underutilized function of the body scan: enhancing positive sensations. Just as you can use phase 5 to install additional elements from the adaptive neural network (as opposed to just installing the PC), you can also use phase 6 to keep enhancing these new, adaptive somatic patterns via the body scan. The enhancement of somatic patterns can be done in many ways. In Schwartz and Maiberger's (2018) book, *EMDR Therapy and Somatic Psychology: Interventions to Enhance Embodiment in Trauma Treatment*, the authors describe numerous interventions that can be incorporated into the body scan. Here are three examples of adaptive somatic patterns that can be enhanced by using the body scan:

- If clients tend to hold their breath, use the body scan to enhance the flow of their new breathing pattern.

- If clients tend to sit with a slumped posture, help them adopt a new posture with their back straight.

- If clients tend to hold tension in their jaw, help them notice this tension by having them slowly open and close their mouth, massage their jaw, and bring awareness to the tension.

How to Integrate Somatic Interventions into the Body Scan

When clients transition from desensitization to installation to body scan, many changes happen. While clients are usually able to recognize the positive changes that occur with their emotions and thinking patterns, they often miss the physiological shifts associated with these cognitive and emotional changes. For example, if a client reports no disturbances but they still have shallow breathing, you can help them scan their body with a deeper, longer breathing pattern. If they are sitting in a slumped position—a physical pattern that is coupled with their old NC—help them correct it by instructing them to sit with a straight back that is correlated with their PC. If, during the body scan, you or the client notices that they are holding tension in the jaw, help them, with guidance and support, to scan their body while noticing and loosening the tension. If necessary, do more than one body scan as you help your client reprogram their adaptive physical sensations.

Phase 7: Leave Time for Closure

The most important thing you want to remember about the closure phase is not to end a session when the client is experiencing high levels of disturbance that they cannot regulate. This can lead to a quick deterioration in their mental state, which can result in suicidal thoughts, risky or unhealthy behaviors, and psychiatric hospitalization. Therefore, make sure to always leave enough time at the end of each session to help your client lower their levels of disturbance.

Closing the session is not limited to the safe place and container exercises. You can also use some of the somatic interventions presented in this chapter, draw on some grounding techniques, meditate with the client, or use other breathing exercises. You can even end a session with an interweave (Parnell, 2006). Or you can simply ask your client what would help them regulate their nervous system. If everything goes well, you want them to leave your office feeling safe and contained.

Some clients will leave the session and return straight to work to check their email or attend meetings. Others will have some time to reflect and do some journaling—an activity I always encourage after an EMDR session, since processing continues between sessions. Make sure to remind clients that since their brain continues to be in "processing mode," journaling provides a wonderful opportunity to reflect on what they learned with you in session. In addition, remind clients that sometimes negative material will continue to surface after a processing session. Help your clients prepare for this possibility and help them formulate a plan: What are they going to do if the disturbance becomes overwhelming? Whom are they going to call? What kind of self-regulation strategies can they use? This type of planning can make the difference between an unpleasant evening and a visit to the psychiatric emergency room.

When a client has an intense session, I also ask them to send me a brief email the next day, preferably in the middle of the day. I want to know how the rest of their day was, how they slept that night, and how they experienced the first half of the day after the session. I explain that an email will help me gain more insight about our work and allow me to understand whether more adaptive material was integrated or more maladaptive material resurfaced. If the client is struggling, I try to see them as soon as possible, or at least have a phone conversation with them.

Although phase 7 provides some guidelines on how to end an EMDR session, since the brain keeps processing after the session ends, working on a target doesn't end there. Even if you processed a target to completion, with a SUD level of 0 and a VOC of 7, you still need to reevaluate the target memory in the next session, which is what you do in the last phase of EMDR: the reevaluation phase.

Phase 8: Conduct the Reevaluation

The last phase of EMDR is a check-in you do with the client at the beginning of each session to inquire about their experience following the previous processing session. You want to know, in detail, what happened to your client after the last session. Did they feel calmer? (This is very common.) Did they feel anxious? (This is also very common.) Did they have nightmares? Did they remember additional memories or details about the target memories they have been processing?

If you can convince your clients to keep a journal, this can be very helpful. Taking notes is important because people often forget thoughts rather quickly—whether it be things discussed in session, dreams they have had, or even certain memories that have resurfaced—and this material can be used later to set up new target memories to process. Most people these days don't keep a physical journal, but there are other ways to keep notes. If the client is not keen on writing, encourage them to take notes on their phone about anything relevant to the processing work that came up between sessions. Even a small amount of information can do wonders in rejogging your clients' memories, which is helpful for evaluating a more accurate state of progress.

The reevaluation phase does not require using any script. When you assess your clients' progress, remember to ask them about how they are doing in general as it pertains to their initial presenting problem, goals, and symptoms—not just specifically about the target memory you've been working on. It's easy to get caught up in individual targets and forget the big picture: the reason why the client came to see you in the first place. Use the reevaluation phase to assess the most recent target memory you've been working on, but also look at the overall treatment plan and the progress your client has made.

Learning and *understanding* the eight phases of EMDR is the first step to mastering the art and science of EMDR. In the next chapter, you will learn a method that will help you take your EMDR practice to the next level: deliberate practice.

CHAPTER 8

Deliberate Practice

. . . .

Practice isn't the thing you do once you're good.
It's the thing you do that makes you good.

—Malcolm Gladwell, *Outliers: The Story of Success*

. . . .

In his book *Talent Is Overrated*, Geoff Colvin (2008) notes that "extensive research in a wide range of fields shows that many people not only fail to become outstandingly good at what they do, no matter how many years they spend doing it, they frequently don't even get any better than they were when they started" (p. 2). Therapists are no exception: Most of us are okay at what we do. We go through the motions and get by with relative success. We see some of our clients get better. We're more or less satisfied with our performance. We don't get any worse, but most of us don't get much better over the years either.

The main reason for this is that, like most people, we tend to stay in our comfort zone, where we feel in control. But the comfort zone is where we spin our wheels without moving forward. In this way, the comfort zone is the enemy of skill improvement. When we're in this zone, we're not becoming better EMDR therapists.

So how do we get out of our comfort zone? If you're thinking that skills training will get you out of your comfort zone and help you become a better EMDR therapist, you'd only be partially correct. That's because the skills training most of us are familiar with is rarely effective at making us better therapists.

Consider Kalia, an EMDR therapist who recently finished her basic training. As many therapists do, Kalia understands how effective EMDR can be in helping her clients and is enthusiastic about the therapy. She is eager to learn more. She goes to a consultation group once a month, signs up for advanced EMDR trainings, and orders several EMDR books. As Kalia learns about many different protocols and techniques, she very quickly becomes overwhelmed by all the information. She gets so many different suggestions that she ends up going back to her comfort zone: talk therapy.

Does this sound familiar? Many EMDR therapists go through a similar process. They have every intention of learning more techniques to get better at their job, but then somewhere along the way, they lose steam and roll to a stop. If this sounds like you, the good news is that you can intentionally change course and get back on track.

In this chapter, you'll learn how to become a better EMDR therapist. I'll discuss how and why advanced trainings fall short and help you look at your own tendencies when it comes to moving from the comfort zone to the learning zone. Most importantly, I'll examine a proven-effective method called deliberate practice, which can transition you from being an okay therapist to a skilled expert. With these steps and tips, I will show you how to continually grow your EMDR practice.

What Is Deliberate Practice?

Many EMDR therapists believe that the key to EMDR mastery is to read more books and take more trainings. While these can help in a limited fashion, many of us read too quickly and speed through trainings, which is not an effective method for improving skills and leads to mediocre progress in most cases. Experts who study peak performance conclude that focusing on deep learning is a much better way to develop and master skills. This is the basis of deliberate practice, also known as deep practice, which is a rigorous and systematic method for improving performance. It has been used in fields as varied as sports, chess, music, and, most recently, psychotherapy.

The term *deliberate practice* was coined by Anders Ericsson and colleagues after studying top-level performers in a wide range of fields to determine what separates experts from most of us (Ericsson & Pool, 2016). After three decades of research, they made an interesting discovery: Top performers, no matter their field, follow a very similar process of learning and practice that is very different from how the average person learns and practices. In particular, they concluded that the most accomplished musicians, surgeons, pilots, athletes, and other professionals do the following:

- Define very specific goals for their practice

- Focus on a specific technique or skill

- Get (and integrate) feedback on their performance

- Repeat the process until skill development is achieved

To achieve mastery, elite performers practice "in a focused way, with clear goals, a plan for reaching those goals, and a way to monitor [their] progress" (Ericsson & Pool, 2016, p. 22). To continually improve their performance, they break down very specific goals into small increments, they have a coach or a teacher who gives them constant feedback, and they engage in a lot of repetition. This is the essence of deliberate practice.

When EMDR therapists start practicing this way—with focus and intent—not only do they become more confident in what they do, but they develop a new set of skills that makes them better. I have witnessed this process firsthand—EMDR therapists going from scared and overwhelmed to confident and skilled—in individual and group consultations. It is not magic. It's simply deliberate practice. By utilizing it, you can take your EMDR practice to a whole different level.

Five Steps to Master a Skill

Mastering a new skill takes work and effort, but the methodical approach of deliberate practice can help you solidify whatever you're learning and excel at whatever technique is before you. Here are the steps to becoming an expert at any new skill:

1. Practice.

2. Integrate feedback.

3. Make micro-adjustments based on that feedback.

4.   Practice micro-adjustments.

5.   Assess your improvement.

Although people tend to think about most things in a linear way (think: the eight phases of EMDR), the best way to understand deliberate practice is to think of it as a cyclical model. Once you master a skill, you don't stop growing; you move on to learning a new skill (or a protocol or technique). You keep practicing, you keep getting feedback, and you keep making small adjustments based on the feedback you're receiving.

Making these micro-adjustments is a key undertaking when applying deliberate practice. If you're trying too many things at once (as therapists are prone to do when they're trying a new protocol for the first time in session), you are multitasking, and therefore, not focused. You also may be making too large an adjustment all at once; when this happens, you are more likely to make one big clumsy change instead of several small, adroit adjustments. To practice deliberately, you need to focus on making micro-adjustments based on the feedback you're getting.

So if the evidence shows that you need to practice—a lot—to be great at something, it makes sense to apply the principle of deliberate practice to your work as an EMDR therapist. This is how you become an expert. Like Mozart, Michael Jordan, Itzhak Perlman, and other top performers, you can follow this proven method for success. The rest of this chapter will show you how to engage in deliberate practice when it comes to your EMDR trainings and consultations.

Setting Yourself Up for Success

Stay in the Learning Zone

Top performers achieve excellence by constantly pushing the limits of their practice. They practice skills in the sweet spot known as the *learning zone*—where they're a little outside what's comfortable but not so uncomfortable that learning is negated. In this zone, they can continuously stretch their abilities. In order to prepare for deliberate practice, it's important for you, too, to make a commitment to crawling out of your comfort zone and entering the learning zone. This is where you want to spend your time and energy when practicing new EMDR skills.

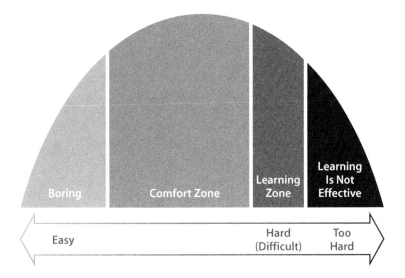

You can think of the learning zone as the window of tolerance for learning. Just like you want to keep your clients in the window of tolerance for effective EMDR processing, you want to be in your personal learning zone to maximize the effectiveness of learning and to improve your skills.

Slow Down

When working with clients, you may feel as if you always have to do or say the "right" thing. However, to achieve excellence as an EMDR therapist, it's necessary to slow down, allow yourself to make mistakes, notice these mistakes, and then correct them. This is very different from running on autopilot, in which you're going through the motions of therapy without conscious awareness of any errors you might be making. Practicing without moment-to-moment awareness does not support learning and is not helpful when you try to learn a new protocol or any other technique.

Keep Your Phone Off

Deliberate practice requires intense concentration and can't be done without focused attention. Keeping your phone on will inevitably result in messages, emails, and other interruptions. This is not an advantageous environment for skill improvement. Turn off your phone and any other devices that might distract you for the duration of your practice. Your text messages can wait.

Eliminate the Noise

In a world of endless distractions, it's easy to get lost in the noise, and it can be hard to stay on task. You might think you're in the learning zone, but you might actually be down a rabbit hole instead. It's easy to get lost in an ocean of books, trainings, protocols, and PDFs. But you must learn to see these as distractions that prevent you from exploring anything in depth. Focusing—and refocusing—on one goal at a time while engaging in deep practice is the best way to take your EMDR to the next level.

A good trainer, consultant, or coach will help you stay on task while continuously assessing where you are in the learning zone. Just as a good therapist helps clients stay in the window of tolerance to get better EMDR results, a good mentor will skillfully assess where you are in the sweet spot of learning and help you optimize your work.

EMDR Trainings Done Better

Most of us attend trainings with the very best of intentions. We learn a new skill or technique at a training and then try what we've learned with our clients without practicing it first. Unfortunately, this method doesn't serve you or your clients well. But you're not entirely at fault; shouldering most of the blame are the trainings themselves.

Think about an advanced EMDR training you've taken: Did you have many opportunities to practice during the training? Were you encouraged to practice afterward? Did you have post-training consultations to practice what you'd learned? I'm guessing your answer to most of these questions is no. The structure of most EMDR trainings is not supported by the science of learning and performance.

Here are some typical EMDR training pitfalls: The PowerPoint presentation is way too long, there is too much information, the practice period is too short or may even be missing, and feedback is almost nonexistent. Instead of focusing on the most important aspects of developing a skill—practice and feedback—many trainers focus on irrelevant facts that are not conducive to learning and to the use of skills or techniques (e.g., who invented a certain protocol and in what year). These trainings are usually not a good return on your investment.

For example, a few years ago, I went to an advanced EMDR training and spent the whole morning watching a PowerPoint presentation that had too many slides about the hypothalamic-pituitary-adrenal (HPA) axis. When it came time to practice that afternoon, I thought, *Great! Finally, a training with practice.* But the trainer did not check on us. Not even once. The trainer did not provide any feedback about the new skills we were acquiring. As mentioned, this training was not a good return on my investment.

This isn't meant as a criticism of any individual EMDR trainer; it is an invitation to the EMDR community to reevaluate the current model of teaching. Most EMDR trainers (who are usually experienced EMDR clinicians) spend a lot of time learning the ins and outs of EMDR and the neurobiology of trauma, but when it comes to the science of learning and deliberate practice, most are either not aware of the data or simply disregard it.

Therefore, make sure to research and attend trainings that give you the best return on your investment. Take ones that will make you a better EMDR therapist—those that include practice and feedback. For the training to be effective, the trainer must provide direct, real-time feedback with specific suggestions on how you can improve your practice. The trainer should then watch you practice, based on their feedback, and offer more feedback. Getting and integrating feedback is key: If you keep making the same mistake and nobody tells you it's a mistake, how will you learn? Imagine a surgeon who learned how to perform operations by watching a PowerPoint presentation and watching a couple of videos. Would you let this person perform their first operation on you? Likewise, I don't recommend trying a new technique with clients without practicing and getting feedback first.

Some EMDR trainers even offer post-training consultations. These are great, and I highly recommend taking advantage of them if they're available to you. If these are not offered, try to create your own follow-up learning plan after each training.

EMDR Consultations Done Better

Here is how most EMDR consultation groups happen:

- You join a group of four to six people.

- Every few weeks, you present a client case for advice.

- Your consultant tells you what they think you need to do.

- Sometimes your consultant sends you a file with more information.

- A few days later, you try the new technique or protocol in session.

- You try to remember what exactly you were supposed to do.

- In most cases, you improvise something from memory.

- A week or two later, you're back in consultation group with no follow-up.

Whether you are in a group or working individually with an EMDR consultant or coach, make sure you get the most out of these meetings. Whenever possible, spend time watching videos during the consultation. These videos can be real sessions that were recorded with clients' permission or practice sessions you've done with a colleague. Videos provide a lot of data. Through them, you can more easily and carefully observe clients' body language, their breath patterns, and the slight changes in their tone of voice—all information that you tend to miss in real time.

The amount of extra information can then make it easier to make micro-adjustments. You determine what you could have done better in the session and practice that with your consultant, coach, or fellow EMDR group members. You continue to receive feedback and make slight changes based on their feedback. If you're trying to learn a new skill, technique, or protocol, you also practice that during the consultation through the use of role-plays. Role-plays are very effective when trying to learn new protocols and are useful to enhance learning and skill development. Essentially, the goal is to get feedback, keep practicing, and get more feedback.

EMDR Done Better

I hope that, by now, I have convinced you that practice is necessary for developing new skills. Deliberate practice, however, is very different from any other practice you have done before. To apply the rules of deliberate practice to therapy and take your EMDR practice to the next level, you will need to:

1. Identify a specific skill you want to work on.

2. Analyze recordings of your sessions.

3. Practice the basics first.

4. Integrate feedback.

5. Retain a growth mindset.

6. Choose a competent consultant.

Let's explore each of these steps in detail.

Identify a Specific Skill

In *The Little Book of Talent*, Daniel Coyle (2012) distinguishes between two types of skills:

- **Hard, high-precision skills:** These skills need to be performed in a consistent way every time. To get the best result, you have to repeat the exact same thing.

- **Soft, high-flexibility skills:** These skills have many paths to the best result and are not as rigid. To get the best result with soft skills, you have to be flexible.

The most effective EMDR clinicians master both the hard and the soft skills. You have to master the hard skills first before moving on to the soft ones. Hard skills require repetition (e.g., repeating the standard protocol when you first learn it), while soft skills involve recognizing patterns, body language, and nonverbal communication (e.g., recognizing when clients are out of their window of tolerance). Coyle (2012) notes that "while hard skills are best put together with measured precision, soft skills are built by playing and exploring inside a challenging, ever-changing environment" (p. 29). Your clients are always in an "ever-changing environment," which is why you need to master these soft skills. Let me give you an example.

In basic EMDR training, you learned that when reevaluating a target, you go back to the same memory to continue working on the target. But as you process target memories with your clients, you will sometimes find that a client will report a SUD level of 0 with the original memory and that the real disturbance is associated with an event that happened around the time of the initial target. So what do you do?

The answer is that there is no one answer and that you need to be attentive to your clients, their needs, and their disturbance. You need to figure out when to go back to the original target and when to develop a new one. There is no one-size-fits-all answer here, which is why it is essential to master your EMDR soft skills.

Analyze Recordings of Your Sessions

When therapists start their EMDR journey, they often fumble before getting the hang of things. Improvisation is popular among newly trained EMDR therapists, who often describe experiencing impostor syndrome. They fear making mistakes that will harm their clients. This fear is valid, since some errors can lead to the deterioration of clients' mental states (e.g., keeping the processing going when your clients dissociate), but without feedback, therapists will keep making the same mistakes without realizing it.

You can avoid this happening to you by analyzing recordings of your sessions (with clients' permission, of course) and sharing them with a consultant. Think of a client who reports an intense feeling of shame, and their therapist tells them to "just notice that" for 12 consecutive sets. Without knowing it, the therapist is reinforcing the client's shame. This situation would be easily recognized by a consultant watching a video of the session, but the consultant is likely to miss this information if the therapist just describes the session to their consultant from memory.

If you work with a consultant, ask them to give you feedback on very specific things. Ask them to notice the smallest errors and to stop the video every time they detect a mistake—or every time they have a suggestion for a different intervention. You don't want your consultant to wait until the end of the video to provide feedback because the information they are providing you needs to be about *specific* errors. General feedback ("You did great" or "You need to improve your target selection") is not useful. Your consultant needs to provide concrete, actionable feedback about specific mistakes. Make sure you write down these mistakes and your consultant's accompanying feedback (along with the time stamp) so you can rewatch the video later with the comments you've written.

Typically, watching your sessions with an EMDR consultant is more beneficial than watching them alone because they have a deeper understanding of what you are trying to master, and they will notice more of your errors or places for improvement than you would alone. However, if a consultant isn't available to join you, watching recorded sessions on your own can still be effective. It will allow you to notice errors in your target selection and in the way you respond to clients that you weren't aware of in real time. For example, when watching a recording, you may notice that a client had been looping in session and that you didn't use an interweave for nine consecutive sets.

Watching videos of your sessions and detecting errors can feel like finishing a 100-mile bike ride—it's challenging, for sure, but it also gives you a deep sense of satisfaction. Focusing on the skills or techniques you need to improve, or on mistakes you've made, is a little like going uphill. It can be hard in the moment, but it is the best way to get stronger.

Practice the Basics First

Many newly trained therapists are so excited about EMDR that they sign up for advanced training shortly after finishing their basic training. This is not an effective approach to learning and improving your EMDR skills. Just as expert pianists didn't start playing Bach before they learned notes, chords, and rhythm, you can't master the DeTUR protocol or integrate ego state work into your EMDR practice before you master the standard protocol—which you can only do with practice.

Therefore, before you sign up for advanced EMDR trainings and try to integrate different therapeutic approaches, like IFS or sensorimotor psychotherapy, you need to practice, get feedback, and practice again. You need to memorize the standard protocol. You need to have a handle on your hard skills. Essentially, you need to feel completely confident and in control with the basic EMDR protocol. Only then is it time to move on. This is the same approach I take when working with consultees who recently finished their basic EMDR training; we first practice the basics.

Integrate Feedback

In his book *Deliberate Practice for Psychotherapists*, Tony Rousmaniere (2016) reminds us that, unlike many other professionals, therapists work "largely in secret and isolation, sheltered from any performance feedback besides our own self-perceptions" (p. 93). But self-perceptions are not enough if you want to be better. You have to get feedback, and you have to integrate this new information by doing something with it.

There's an important distinction between getting feedback and integrating feedback. When you *get* feedback, you can be passive about it. You can avoid using it, or you can plan to do something with it in the future—and then get busy with other tasks. But when you *integrate* feedback, you are being proactive about learning. You practice the new skill you are trying to improve while making small, incremental adjustments to your approach. And most importantly, you keep getting and integrating more feedback.

Retain a Growth Mindset

When you start integrating deliberate practice into your EMDR consultations, you may feel uncomfortable. You may also feel like you're failing. This is normal because deliberate practice is hard, and it can even be painful. The important thing is to remind yourself that feedback is a measure of potential, not failure. The worst thing you can do is skip feedback because it's uncomfortable. Good consultants or trainers who provide you with feedback are doing so not because they want to bring you down, but because they want you to succeed. Remember that feedback is how you learn and how you become the EMDR therapist your clients deserve.

In order to improve your EMDR practice, you need to retain a growth mindset. Instead of running away from your mistakes, being ashamed of the mistakes you've made, or viewing your mistakes as evidence of your failures as a therapist, you need to develop a growth mindset in which you view errors as opportunities for growth. Because focusing on what you're not good at (yet) is uncomfortable—and because we are creatures that seek comfort—deliberate practice is the opposite of what most of us usually do. But ego is the enemy of skill development. Deliberate practice helps us learn from our mistakes, improve our practice, and provide better care for our clients.

Choose a Competent Consultant

When choosing an EMDR consultant, you'll likely find that many consultants and trainers differ widely in their opinions about how to do EMDR. The problem is not with different opinions but with what many EMDR consultants and trainers do with their opinions: They consider them as facts and teach them as absolute truths (Marich, 2021). Be suspicious of any consultant (or any person, for that matter) who claims to know everything or who gives you the same answer to every question you ask. Some consultants will tell you that the answer to every problem you have in your EMDR work is in the case formulation. Others will tell you that it's all about the parts. But the same answer to every problem can't possibly be right.

When a trainer or consultant teaches you rigid facts about EMDR that don't sit well with you, get a second opinion. And when your consultant warns you that "this is the only right way to do EMDR," challenge them. Clients are complex individuals, so you want to work with a consultant who understands complexity. Be careful of consultants with a one-size-fits-all approach.

If your consultant is not aware of the science of deliberate practice, educate them. The resources provided at the end of this book have helped some of my own consultants understand the importance of this approach. If your consultant is still not open to the process, consider finding a different consultant.

Finally, if your EMDR consultant is a super-nice kind of person and always tells you how well you are doing, you might find that they're better at friendship than feedback. They may be a person you trust or even someone you have a great personal relationship with, but if they are not a good fit for you, the consultant-therapist relationship will not benefit your EMDR work. To get the most out of your consultations, you'll need real-time constructive feedback about areas for improvement. Work with a consultant who can help you notice your errors and turn them into skills. Look for someone who can challenge you.

Getting into the Habit of Deliberate Practice

As I mentioned, engaging in deep practice to grow your EMDR therapy skills is not fun, is not easy, and takes time out of your busy day—at the end of the day, EMDR is work, even if you have a passion for learning about it and using it to better your clients' lives. Deliberate practice requires intense focus—so intense that you feel exhausted afterward. It leaves less time for watching Netflix and checking Facebook, activities that are a lot more inherently enjoyable. So how do you give up the fun activities—those activities that help you relax after a long day of seeing clients—and instead practice something that is not enjoyable?

Deliberate decisions start with setting priorities. Practicing deliberately as an EMDR therapist, as an athlete, or as a musician always starts with thinking in advance about what you want to achieve and who you want to become instead of focusing on what's fun in the moment. In other words, deliberate practice starts with your "why." It starts with the very important reason why you want to spend hours, across several months and years, doing something that is not fun. The only way to do that is to find a strong internal motivation that is based on your values.

For me, the satisfaction of seeing my clients achieve adaptive resolution serves as a reminder of why I do what I do. For you, perhaps this motivation stems from seeing your clients heal from trauma, recover from addictions, and live their lives to the fullest. Whatever your "why" is, you have to find ways to keep this motivation going, because unlike social media and streaming services—which offer an immediate rush of dopamine that feels more enjoyable than watching a video of yourself making mistakes while trying a new protocol—deliberate practice takes time and consistency. It doesn't happen on its own. So it's important to keep reminding yourself why you're doing this work when Netflix and Facebook are just a click away.

The Path to EMDR Mastery

I started this book by talking about how you can use EMDR to rewire your clients' traumatized brains and help them heal. I want to end by encouraging you to consider rewiring your own brain with deliberate practice. You know from reading this book that repetition is necessary for skill development. And this repetition is what leads to the very neural rewiring I'm talking about. By engaging in repeated practice, your brain produces more myelin around specific neural networks, and this accumulation of myelin allows them to fire faster, with less effort.

This effortless firing is what happens when a professional becomes an expert. It's what happens when world-class tennis players can predict, with accuracy, where the ball is going to land before their opponent even hits the ball, just by observing their body. The expert tennis player develops an extraordinary ability to read body language and can make a prediction just by looking, for a split second, at their opponent's movement.

Like that tennis player, you can become a skilled EMDR therapist who picks up your clients' nonverbal cues and does so faster than your less-skilled counterparts. You can become a therapist who knows when to change gears in the processing phases instead of going around in circles with the same rigid technique. A therapist who knows the protocol and also the importance of individualizing it to clients' needs. By increasing myelination, you can change your own brain and master the art and science of EMDR.

Although this book just represents a starting point on your journey, I hope it has given you the tools you need to become a more confident and effective EMDR therapist. But remember that this book alone cannot make you a better therapist. The path to EMDR mastery is to put the lessons in this book into practice. You must practice, practice, practice so the same neural circuits repeatedly fire together, allowing them to become stronger and faster over time. This book has shown you the way—now it's up to you to start the journey.

....

Resources

....

Articles and Podcasts

Ericsson, K. A., Prietula, M. J., & Cokely, E. T. (2007, July–August). The making of an expert. *Harvard Business Review*. https://hbr.org/2007/07/the-making -of-an-expert

  » Written in a user-friendly style, and citing many examples, this *Harvard Business Review* article describes why "not all practice makes perfect" and what it takes to become an expert.

Gawande, A. (2011, September 26). Personal best: Top athletes and singers have coaches. Should you? *The New Yorker*. https://www.newyorker.com/magazine /2011/10/03/personal-best

  » Atul Gawande explores the role of coaching in deliberate practice and describes how he—an experienced surgeon—hired a coach to help him improve his work performance. He concludes that a good coach not only teaches you how to perform but also teaches you how to think.

Marich, J. (2021, May 26). An open letter to the EMDR community: Stop passing off your opinions as facts. *The Institute for Creative Mindfulness*. https://www .instituteforcreativemindfulness.com/icm-blog-redefine-therapy/an-open -letter-to-the-emdr-community-stop-passing-off-your-opinions-as-facts/

  » Dr. Jamie Marich suggests ending the spread of EMDR-related misinformation and disinformation, and encourages EMDR consultants and trainers to challenge their own belief systems. She concludes that opinions, even very strong ones, should not be considered facts.

Savage, J., Sundwall, M., & Falkentien, B. (Hosts). (2021, June 2). State change vs. trait change (No. 51) [Audio podcast episode]. In *Notice that.* Patreon. https://emdr-podcast.com/episode-51-state-change-vs-trait-change/

>> In this rich and engaging conversation, which touches on concepts from interpersonal neurobiology and polyvagal theory, hosts of the *Notice That* podcast, Jen, Melissa, and Bridger, discuss the difference between state change and trait change.

Books

Colvin, G. (2008). *Talent is overrated: What really separates world-class performers from everybody else.* Portfolio.

>> After publishing his mega-popular 2006 *Fortune* article "What It Takes to Be Great," Geoff Colvin expands his thoughts into a book-length study in what it takes to become an elite performer.

Coyle, D. (2009). *The talent code: Greatness isn't born. It's grown. Here's how.* Bantam Books.

>> Using many examples drawn from the worlds of sports and music, bestselling author Daniel Coyle explains how deliberate practice enhances performance.

Coyle, D. (2012). *The little book of talent: 52 tips for improving your skills.* Bantam Books.

>> This book explores the hotbeds of experts in sports, art, and music. Coyle explains what experts in a number of fields do to become experts and provides simple, user-friendly techniques to improve your own practice.

Dalai Lama. (2002). *An open heart: Practicing compassion in everyday life* (N. Vreeland, Ed.). Back Bay Books.

>> This is the Dalai Lama's practical manual to integrating compassion into your life.

Das, L. S. (1998). *Awakening the Buddha within: Eight steps to enlightenment: Tibetan wisdom for the Western world*. Harmony.

» This book reviews the guidelines and principles embodied in the eightfold path and explains how we can apply them to our daily lives.

Duhigg, C. (2012). *The power of habit: Why we do what we do in life and business*. Random House.

» Using simple language and great examples, this book teaches you how to create new habits and break old ones.

Epstein, M. (2018). *Advice not given: A guide to getting over yourself*. Penguin.

» A psychiatrist and a Buddhist teacher, Mark Epstein will help you bring the wisdom of Buddhism into your therapy room.

Ericsson, A., & Pool, R. (2016). *Peak: Secrets from the new science of expertise*. Mariner Books.

» Written by the leading researcher on the science of deliberate practice, this book provides an easy introduction to deliberate practice and what it takes to become a peak performer.

Grant, M. D. (2016). *The new change your brain, change your pain: Based on EMDR*. Trauma and Pain Management Services.

» With years of experience as an EMDR practitioner, Mark Grant introduces a new approach to treating chronic pain based on EMDR and the understanding of how chronic pain is processed in the brain.

Harris, D. (2017). *Meditation for fidgety skeptics: A 10% happier how-to book*. Harmony.

» ABC News anchor Dan Harris shares how an individual with a very busy mind incorporates mindfulness into his daily life. His message is "If I can do it, you can do it."

Lanius, U. F., & Bergmann, U. (2014). Dissociation, EMDR, and adaptive information processing: The role of sensory stimulation and sensory awareness. In U. F. Lanius, S. L. Paulsen, & F. M. Corrigan (Eds.), *Neurobiology and treatment of traumatic dissociation: Toward an embodied self* (pp. 213–242). Springer.

> » In this book chapter, the authors describe, in technical terms, how symptoms of trauma and dissociation develop, and what happens in the brain when integration of information is disrupted. They describe the neurobiological mechanisms of the AIP model and highlight the mechanisms of action of EMDR.

Lemov, D., Woolway, E., & Yezzi, K. (2012). *Practice perfect: 42 rules for getting better at getting better.* Jossey-Bass.

> » Lemov and his colleagues developed a system to help teachers become better at what they do. They describe, in detail, their method of training teachers using the rules of deliberate practice.

Marich, J., & Dansiger, S. (2017). *EMDR therapy and mindfulness for trauma-focused care.* Springer.

> » This is a phenomenal book on how to integrate mindfulness into therapy in general and into EMDR in particular.

Neff, K., & Germer, C. (2018). *The mindful self-compassion workbook: A proven way to accept yourself, build inner strength, and thrive.* Guilford Press.

> » This book covers the theory and practice of self-compassion and includes helpful practices clients can use in and between sessions.

Nestor, J. (2020). *Breath: The new science of a lost art.* Penguin.

> » James Nestor explores the history of the breath from different cultures and shares scientific data, the latest breath research, and the results of his own self-experimentation with different breathing methods.

Pollan, M. (2018). *How to change your mind: What the new science of psychedelics teaches us about consciousness, dying, addiction, depression, and transcendence.* Penguin.

> » In this book, Michael Pollan reviews the history of psychedelics, describes his insightful personal experiences with different types of psychedelics, and explores the therapeutic possibilities of psychedelic-assisted therapy.

Rousmaniere, T. (2016). *Deliberate practice for psychotherapists: A guide to improving clinical effectiveness.* Routledge.

> » This book describes author Tony Rousmaniere's experiences implementing deliberate practice into his own psychotherapy practice and supervision.

Servan-Schreiber, D. (2005). *Healing without Freud or Prozac: Natural approaches to curing stress, anxiety, and depression without drugs and without psychoanalysis.* Pan Macmillan.

> » This book details natural healing processes that don't involve medication or psychoanalysis. (Chapters 5 and 6 are dedicated to EMDR.)

Tarrant, J. (2017). *Meditation interventions to rewire the brain: Integrating neuroscience strategies for ADHD, anxiety, depression & PTSD.* PESI Publishing.

> » A pioneer in the field of neuromeditation, Jeff Tarrant reviews brain science and gives practical advice on how to individualize meditation to your clients' needs.

Wright, R. (2017). *Why Buddhism is true: The science and philosophy of meditation and enlightenment.* Simon and Schuster.

> » Robin Wright helps us understand where Buddhist concepts can be integrated into daily life in easy, simple language.

Studies

Chow, D. L., Miller, S. D., Seidel, J. A., Kane, R. T., Thornton, J. A., & Andrews, W. P. (2015). The role of deliberate practice in the development of highly effective psychotherapists. *Psychotherapy, 52*(3), 337–345. https://doi.org/10.1037/pst0000015

Ericsson, K. A., Krampe, R. T., & Tesch-Romer, C. (1993). The role of deliberate practice in the acquisition of expert performance. *Psychological Review, 100*(3), 363–406. https://doi.org/10.1037/0033-295X.100.3.363

Farina, B., Imperatori, C., Quintiliani, M. I., Castelli Gattinara, P., Onofri, A., Lepore, M., Brunetti, R., Losurdo, A., Testani, E., & Della Marca, G. (2015). Neurophysiological correlates of eye movement desensitization and reprocessing sessions: Preliminary evidence for traumatic memories integration. *Clinical Physiology and Functional Imaging, 35*(6), 460–468. https://doi.org/10.1111/cpf.12184

Fleck, J. I., Olsen, R., Tumminia, M., DePalma, F., Berroa, J., Vrabel, A., & Miller, S. (2018). Changes in brain connectivity following exposure to bilateral eye movements. *Brain and Cognition, 123*, 142–153. https://doi.org/10.1016/j.bandc.2018.03.009

Gotink, R. A., Meijboom, R., Vernooij, M. W., Smits, M., & Hunink, M. M. (2016). 8-week mindfulness based stress reduction induces brain changes similar to traditional long-term meditation practice—A systematic review. *Brain and Cognition, 108*, 32–41. https://doi.org/10.1016/j.bandc.2016.07.001

Hölzel, B. K., Carmody, J., Evans, K. C., Hoge, E. A., Dusek, J. A., Morgan, L., Pitman, R. K., & Lazar, S. W. (2010). Stress reduction correlates with structural changes in the amygdala. *Social Cognitive and Affective Neuroscience, 5*(1), 11–17. https://doi.org/10.1093/scan/nsp034

Kuiken, D., Chudleigh, M., & Racher, D. (2010). Bilateral eye movements, attentional flexibility and metaphor comprehension: The substrate of REM dreaming? *Dreaming, 20*(4), 227–247. https://doi.org/10.1037/a0020841

Lansing, K., Amen, D. G., Hanks, C., & Rudy, L. (2005). High-resolution brain SPECT imaging and eye movement desensitization and reprocessing in police officers with PTSD. *Journal of Neuropsychiatry and Clinical Neurosciences, 17*(4), 526–532. https://doi.org/10.1176/jnp.17.4.526

Lyle, K. B., & Martin, J. M. (2010). Bilateral saccades increase intrahemispheric processing but not interhemispheric interaction: Implications for saccade-induced retrieval enhancement. *Brain and Cognition, 73*(2), 128–134. https://doi.org/10.1016/j.bandc.2010.04.004

Richardson, P., Williams, S. C. R., Hepenstall, S., Gregory, L. J., McKie, S., & Corrigan, F. (2009). A single-case fMRI study EMDR treatment of a patient with posttraumatic stress disorder. *Journal of EMDR Practice and Research, 3*(1), 10–23. https://doi.org/10.1891/1933-3196.3.1.10

Rousseau, P. F., Boukezzi, S., Garcia, R., Chaminade, T., & Khalfa, S. (2020). Cracking the EMDR code: Recruitment of sensory, memory and emotional networks during bilateral alternating auditory stimulation. *Australian & New Zealand Journal of Psychiatry, 54*(8), 818–831. https://doi.org/10.1177/0004867420913623

Stickgold, R. (2002). EMDR: A putative neurobiological mechanism of action. *Journal of Clinical Psychology, 58*(1), 61–75. https://doi.org/10.1002/jclp.1129

Trautwein, F. M., Kanske, P., Böckler, A., & Singer, T. (2020). Differential benefits of mental training types for attention, compassion, and theory of mind. *Cognition, 194*, Article 104039. https://doi.org/10.1016/j.cognition.2019.104039

Meditation Apps

» **Calm:** A paid app with daily meditations, relaxation music, and before-bed practices

» **Dharma Seed:** A free app with hundreds of dharma talks with prominent teachers like Joseph Goldstein and Tara Brach

» **Headspace:** A paid app with a library of more than 500 meditations, on everything from stress to resilience to compassion

Meditation Devices

» **HeartMath:** A biofeedback device therapists can use in sessions to observe real-time feedback from the nervous system and to teach clients new skills. HeartMath can also be used by clients outside of therapy sessions.

» **Muse:** A device clients can use to track their meditation progress. The Muse app is attached to the Muse device via Bluetooth and provides real-time feedback on the quality of the meditation and helps users refocus when their thoughts start drifting.

Mindfulness Scripts and Guided Audio

» **Simple mindful breath meditation script:** Guide your clients in an easy breathwork meditation by using this script: https://emdartnscience .com/book.

» **Simple mindful breath meditation guided audio:** Listen to this recording to ease into your own breathwork meditation: https://emdartnscience .com/book.

References

Badenoch, B. (2008). *Being a brain-wise therapist: A practical guide to interpersonal neurobiology.* W. W. Norton.

Baldwin, M., & Korn, D. (2021). *Every memory deserves respect: EMDR, the proven trauma therapy with the power to heal.* Workman.

Baldwin, S. A., Wampold, B. E., & Imel, Z. E. (2007). Untangling the alliance-outcome correlation: Exploring the relative importance of therapist and patient variability in the alliance. *Journal of Consulting and Clinical Psychology, 75*(6), 842–852. https://doi.org/10.1037/0022-006X.75.6.842

Calancie, O. G., Khalid-Khan, S., Booij, L., & Munoz, D. P. (2018). Eye movement desensitization and reprocessing as a treatment for PTSD: Current neurobiological theories and a new hypothesis. *Annals of the New York Academy of Sciences, 1426*(1), 127–145. https://doi.org/10.1111/nyas.13882

Cayton-Holland, A. (2018). *Tragedy plus time: A tragi-comic memoir.* Gallery Books.

Childre, D., & Rozman, D. (2005). *Transforming stress: The HeartMath solution for relieving worry, fatigue, and tension.* New Harbinger.

Colvin, G. (2008). *Talent is overrated: What really separates world-class performers from everybody else.* Penguin.

Cowan, W. M., & Kandel, E. R. (2001). A brief history of synapses and synaptic transmission. In W. M. Cowan, T. C. Südhof, & C. F. Stevens (Eds.), *Synapses* (pp. 1–88). Johns Hopkins University Press.

Coyle, D. (2012). *The little book of talent: 52 tips for improving your skills.* Bantam Books.

Cozolino, L. (2015). *Why therapy works: Using our minds to change our brains.* W. W. Norton.

Cozolino, L. (2017). *The neuroscience of psychotherapy: Healing the social brain* (2nd ed.). W. W. Norton.

Das, L. S. (1998). *Awakening the Buddha within: Eight steps to enlightenment: Tibetan wisdom for the Western world*. Harmony.

de Voogd, L. D., Kanen, J. W., Neville, D. A., Roelofs, K., Fernández, G., & Hermans, E. J. (2018). Eye-movement intervention enhances extinction via amygdala deactivation. *Journal of Neuroscience, 38*(40), 8694–8706. https://doi.org/10.1523/JNEUROSCI.0703-18.2018

Doidge, N. (2007). *The brain that changes itself: Stories of personal triumph from the frontiers of brain science*. Penguin Life.

Doidge, N. (2015). *The brain's way of healing: Remarkable discoveries and recoveries from the frontiers of neuroplasticity*. Penguin Life.

Duhigg, C. (2014). *The power of habit. Why we do what we do in life and business*. Random House.

Ericsson, A., & Pool, R. (2016). *Peak: Secrets from the new science of expertise*. Mariner Books.

Gelbard-Sagiv, H., Mukamel, R., Harel, M., Malach, R., & Fried, I. (2008). Internally generated reactivation of single neurons in human hippocampus during free recall. *Science, 322*(5898), 96–101. https://doi.org/10.1126/science.1164685

Gladwell, M. (2011). *Outliers: The story of success*. Back Bay Books.

Goleman, D., & Davidson, R. J. (2018). *Altered traits: Science reveals how meditation changes your mind, brain, and body*. Avery.

Harris, D. (2017). *Meditation for fidgety skeptics: A 10% happier how-to book*. Harmony.

Hebb, D. O. (1949). *The organization of behaviour*. Wiley.

Hensley, B. J. (2016). *An EMDR therapy primer: From practicum to practice* (2nd ed.). Springer.

Kabat-Zinn, J. (2005). *Wherever you go, there you are: Mindfulness meditation in everyday life*. Hachette Books.

Knipe, J. (2018). *EMDR toolbox: Theory and treatment of complex PTSD and dissociation* (2nd ed.). Springer.

Levine, P. A. (2015). *Trauma and memory: Brain and body in a search for the living past: A practical guide for understanding and working with traumatic memory.* North Atlantic Books.

Lipke, H. (1999). *EMDR and psychotherapy integration: Theoretical and clinical suggestions with focus on traumatic stress.* CRC Press.

Manfield, P. (1998). *Extending EMDR: A casebook of innovative applications.* W. W. Norton.

Manfield, P. (2013). *EMDR up close: Subtleties of trauma processing.* CreateSpace Independent Publishing Platform.

Marich, J. (2021, May 26). An open letter to the EMDR community: Stop passing off your opinions as facts. *The Institute for Creative Mindfulness.* https://www.instituteforcreativemindfulness.com/icm-blog-redefine-therapy/an-open-letter-to-the-emdr-community-stop-passing-off-your-opinions-as-facts/

Marich, J. (2023). *Dissociation made simple: A stigma-free guide to embracing your dissociative mind and navigating daily life.* North Atlantic Books.

Marich, J., & Dansiger, S. (2017). *EMDR therapy and mindfulness for trauma-focused care.* Springer.

Marich, J., & Dansiger, S. (2021). *Healing addiction with EMDR therapy: A trauma-focused guide.* Springer.

Matthijssen, S. J., Brouwers, T., van Roozendaal, C., Vuister, T., & de Jongh, A. (2021). The effect of EMDR versus EMDR 2.0 on emotionality and vividness of aversive memories in a non-clinical sample. *European Journal of Psychotraumatology, 12*(1), Article 1956793. https://doi.org/10.1080/20008198.2021.1956793

Neff, K., & Germer, C. (2018). *The mindful self-compassion workbook: A proven way to accept yourself, build inner strength, and thrive.* Guilford Press.

Nestor, J. (2020). *Breath: The new science of a lost art.* Riverhead Books.

Norcross, J. C. (Ed.). (2011). *Psychotherapy relationships that work: Evidence-based responsiveness* (2nd ed.). Oxford University Press.

Orlinsky, D. E., Rønnestad, M. H., & Willutzki, U. (2004). Fifty years of psychotherapy process-outcome research: Continuity and change. In M. J. Lambert (Ed.), *Bergin and Garfield's handbook of psychotherapy and behavior change* (5th ed., pp. 307–390). Wiley.

Parnell, L. (1997). *Transforming trauma: EMDR: The revolutionary new therapy for freeing the mind, clearing the body, and opening the heart.* W. W. Norton.

Parnell, L. (2006). *A therapist's guide to EMDR: Tools and techniques for successful treatment.* W. W. Norton.

Parnell, L. (2013). *Attachment-focused EMDR: Healing relational trauma.* W. W. Norton.

Parnell, L. (2018). *Rewiring the addicted brain: An EMDR-based treatment model for overcoming addictive disorders.* Green Tara Books.

Pollan, M. (2018). *How to change your mind: What the new science of psychedelics teaches us about consciousness, dying, addiction, depression, and transcendence.* Penguin.

Raichle, M. E., MacLeod, A. M., Snyder, A. Z., Powers, W. J., Gusnard, D. A., & Shulman, G. L. (2001). A default mode of brain function. *Proceedings of the National Academy of Sciences of the United States, 98*(2), 676–682. https://doi.org/10.1073/pnas.98.2.676

Rosoff, A. L. (2019). How we do what we do: The therapist, EMDR, and treatment of complex trauma. *Journal of EMDR Practice and Research, 13*(1), 61–74. https://doi.org/10.1891/1933-3196.13.1.61

Rousmaniere, T. (2016). *Deliberate practice for psychotherapists: A guide to improving clinical effectiveness.* Routledge.

Schmidt, S. J. (2020). *Ego state therapy interventions to prepare attachment-wounded adults for EMDR.* Author.

Schore, A. N. (2012). *The science of the art of psychotherapy.* W. W. Norton.

Schore, A. N. (2015). *Affect regulation and the origin of the self: The neurobiology of emotional development.* Routledge.

Schwartz, A., & Maiberger, B. (2018). *EMDR therapy and somatic psychology: Interventions to enhance embodiment in trauma treatment.* W. W. Norton.

Servan-Schreiber, D. (2005). *Healing without Freud or Prozac: Natural approaches to curing stress, anxiety, and depression without drugs and without psychoanalysis.* Pan Macmillan.

Shapiro, F. (2001). *Eye movement desensitization and reprocessing: Basic principles, protocols, and procedures.* Guilford Press.

Shapiro, F. (2013). *Getting past your past: Take control of your life with self-help techniques from EMDR therapy.* Rodale Books.

Shapiro, F. (2018). *Eye movement desensitization and reprocessing: Basic principles, protocols, and procedures* (3rd ed.). Guilford Press.

Siegel, D. J. (1999). *The developing mind: How relationships and the brain interact to shape who we are.* Guilford Press.

Tarrant, J. (2017). *Meditation interventions to rewire the brain: Integrating neuroscience strategies for ADHD, anxiety, depression & PTSD.* PESI Publishing.

van der Kolk, B. (2015). *The body keeps the score: Brain, mind, and body in the healing of trauma.* Penguin.

Yalom, I. D. (1995). *The theory and practice of group psychotherapy* (4th ed.). Basic Books.

Yalom, I. D. (2002). *The gift of therapy: Reflections on being a therapist.* Judy Piatkus Publishers.

Zadra, A., & Stickgold, R. (2021). *When brains dream: Exploring the science and mystery of sleep.* W. W. Norton.

Printed in Great Britain
by Amazon

22195388R00086